8787

Beginner_
Guide to
Gemmology

Beginner's Guides are available on the following subjects:

Amateur Radio
BASIC Programming
Bricklaying
Car Maintenance, Fault-Finding and Repair
Colour Television
Computers
Digital Electronics
Electric Wiring
Electronics
Gemmology
Hi-Fi
Information Technology
Integrated Circuits
Microcomputer Languages
Microcomputers in Business
Microcomputing
Microprocessors
Processing and Printing
Radio
Television
Videocassette Recorders

Beginner's Guide to Gemmology

Peter G. Read

Heinemann Professional Publishing

Heinemann Professional Publishing Ltd
22 Bedford Square, London WC1B 3HH

LONDON MELBOURNE AUCKLAND

First published by Butterworth & Co. (Publishers) Ltd 1980
Reprinted 1981, 1984
First published by Heinemann Professional Publishing Ltd 1988

British Library Cataloguing in Publication Data
Read, Peter G
  Beginner's guide to gemmology
  1. Precious stones
  I. Title
  549 QE392 79–42719

ISBN 0 434 91753 2

Printed and bound in Great Britain by
Butler & Tanner Ltd, Frome and London

Preface

The *Beginner's Guide to Gemmology* has been written to introduce both the newcomer and the student to the fascinating science of gemstones. While the collecting of rough mineral specimens, the design of jewellery and the polishing of gemstones are very popular as hobbies, the more scientific aspects of the basic gem materials are still little understood. Such an understanding is, of course, essential to the student who intends to become a qualified gemmologist, but it can also lead to a better awareness and enjoyment of the subject for the amateur.

The book begins by tracing the growth of the science of gemmology. It then explains the basic qualities necessary in a gem, and goes on to unravel the intricacies of colour, crystallography, hardness, specific gravity, refractive index, pleochroism, critical angle, absorption spectra and luminescence, giving a brief historical background wherever relevant. Gem testing instruments are described, together with their use in the identification of natural gemstones, synthetic gemstones and gemstone simulants. Separate chapters deal with the organic gem materials such as pearl, amber, ivory and coral, and with the techniques used in the production of the man-made gemstones.

The appendices contain profiles of the principal gem materials, together with tables of gemstone constants, a bibliography to assist in further study, and notes relevant to the student who is preparing to take the Preliminary or Diploma examinations of the Gemmological Association of Great Britain.

Peter G. Read

Contents

1 Gemmology, the Science of Gem Materials

Although philosophers, scientists and jewellers have been interested in the characteristics of gemstones for over two thousand years, and books on the subject were in print as long ago as the sixteenth century, it was not until comparatively recently that gemmology became established as a separate science.

One of the events which helped to bring this about was the establishment of the British Gemmological Association, which was founded in 1908 as the Educational Committee of the National Association of Goldsmiths. Further impetus to the growth of the new science was given by the work of pioneers such as Herbert Smith and Bristow Tully who developed some of the first commercial gem testing instruments.

In the early days of gemmology, very few specialised instruments of this type were available to the gemmologist, their initial slow development being due, no doubt, to the very limited demand for such instruments. Today, however, the situation is quite different. The growing consumer market for jewellery has not only increased the number of retail outlets, but also resulted in increased sales of gem testing instruments. This has made the design and manufacture of such instruments economically worthwhile, and they are now produced not only in the UK, but also in the USA, Japan, Belgium, Germany, Switzerland and Italy (*Figure 1.1*).

Another milestone in the development of gemmology was reached in 1925 when Basil Anderson was asked to set up a gem testing laboratory for the London Chamber of Commerce. The

1

laboratory's first task was to devise a means of distinguishing between cultured and natural pearls, but it was soon to become a centre of gemmological research. During the following years, C. J. Payne, R. Webster and A. E. Farn joined the staff of the laboratory, and with Basil Anderson were responsible for the development of many important gem testing techniques which include spectroscopy, X-ray analysis, the use of heavy liquids and luminescence.

Fig. 1.1. A selection from over one hundred items of gem testing equipment

In 1929, Robert M. Shipley received the British Gemmological Association's Diploma, and back in his native America began lecturing on gemmology to the local retail jewellers, and marketing his own correspondence courses on the subject. He then founded the Gemological Institute of America and the American Gem Society, and made them both influential bodies in the growing international world of gemmology.

As the need for a sound knowledge of gemstones spread, gemmological associations were formed in most of the leading gem marketing countries of the world. Despite the proliferation of associations and study courses, however, the high standards of the British Association's examinations have maintained their

Diploma as one of the most valued of gemmological qualifications (i.e. FGA, Fellow of the Gemmological Association).

Because jewellery includes gem materials which have an organic as well as a mineral content, gemmology has become a comprehensive science covering not only mineralogy, geology, optics and chemistry, but also overlapping into the fields of zoology, biology and botany. Among the gem materials used in jewellery, the largest group is that which is derived from the mineral kingdom. The first part of this book therefore deals principally with the characteristics of gemstones having a mineral origin. Gem materials of an organic origin, such as ivory, bone, pearl, coral, tortoiseshell, jet, ebony and amber are described separately in Chapter 10, which also covers the methods of distinguishing them from their simulants.

In the jewellery trade it is often necessary to be able to distinguish a natural gemstone from a synthetic stone or a simulant, and it is this need which gives gemmology its strong practical bias. As new synthetics are introduced, it is the task of the professional gemmologist to discover ways and means of identifying them, and this is now perhaps one of the most exciting and challenging aspects of gemmology.

Apart from its commercial use in gem testing and identification, gemmology also serves the needs of the lapidary and the diamond polisher, as it encompasses such subjects as crystallography, directional hardness and the optics of polished stones. A knowledge of gemstone constants and characteristics can also make the collecting and display of gemstone samples far more interesting to both the amateur gemmologist and the 'rockhound'.

The essential qualities of a gem material

So far we have taken a brief look at the history and diversity of the science of gem materials. Now we must consider the basic qualities that make gemstones and gem materials suitable for use in jewellery. The first and most obvious of these qualities is beauty. Unlike a gemstone's more tangible properties, beauty is not a measurable quantity, but depends mainly on subjective factors associated with the appearance of the stone. If the stone is a transparent coloured gem, the depth of colour and degree of transparency will be the prime factors. With other gems, such as diamond, beauty will be determined by features such as brilliancy, optical purity and the absence of colour, while with precious opal, it will be the iridescent play of colour from beneath the gem's surface that will be the decisive factor.

Rarity is another quality which must be present in some degree in all gemstones. As this is generally the product of supply and demand, the rarity of a stone can be influenced both by fashion and by variations in the availability of the source material. Two examples of these influences can be seen in amber, which is becoming popular again and correspondingly more expensive, and in amethyst, which, until the discovery of the rich South American sources in the eighteenth century, was a rare and costly gemstone.

Although alexandrite is not universally accepted as a particularly beautiful stone, its unusual optical properties and its rarity have now made it one of the most expensive of all the gems. Diamonds are expensive, but as the world production of uncut gem quality diamonds for 1977–8 was in the region of ten million carats, the cost of the finished product is not entirely due to rarity, but is also influenced by the economics of the mining and recovery of the rough stone and the high cost of its polishing and marketing operations.

The third quality which must be present in a gemstone to make it suitable for use in jewellery is its hardness or durability. This is a more practical quality than either beauty or rarity, but without it a gemstone would not be able to withstand either the everyday wear and tear experienced by a piece of jewellery, or the chemical attack from pollutants in the atmosphere, and it would soon lose its surface polish.

Hardness is therefore a most important quality in a gemstone, and its significance in lapidary work, in diamond polishing and in gemstone identification will be discussed fully in Chapter 4.

The terms 'precious' and 'semi-precious' have often been applied to gemstones in an attempt to separate them into two arbitrary valuation categories. Precious gems included the high-value stones such as diamond, ruby, sapphire, alexandrite and emerald, while tourmaline, amethyst, citrine, zircon and peridot were classified as semi-precious. This practice was often meaningless and contradictory, particularly when, for instance, the value of a poor quality ruby was compared with that of a fine peridot.

Today, except perhaps for the purposes of import/export documentation, the terms precious and semi-precious are discouraged in both the jewellery trade and in gemmology, and a gemstone is simply classified as being of gem quality by virtue of its beauty, rarity and durability, regardless of its commercial value.

Gem minerals

At the beginning of this chapter, the word 'mineral' was used to describe one of the groups of gem materials employed in jewellery. Almost all gemstones belong to this group, and it is relevant at this point to explain what is meant by a mineral.

The dictionary definition of the word is 'a substance obtained by mining'. The more precise scientific definition, however, describes it as being a substance which has been formed in the earth's crust by the forces of inorganic (i.e. 'non-living') nature. It is also a homogeneous, or uniform, substance, and has a chemical formula and a set of physical characteristics which are constant throughout its bulk.

In mineralogy, there are several thousand listed minerals, but only about fifty of these have the necessary qualities to make them suitable for use as gems. Within this select group of gem minerals there is a smaller group of metallic minerals. These include gold, silver, platinum and the platinum group metals rhodium and iridium (rhodium is used as a protective plating on silver and iridium is often alloyed with gold or platinum). These precious metals share the distinction with diamond of being chemical elements in their own right, instead of being compounds of elements as are all other gem materials.

Rock and gemstone formation

Although minerals are mined from the earth's crust in various states of purity, the bulk of this crust is made up of various mixtures of minerals which are classified as rocks. Granite, for example, is a relatively common rock which is composed of a mixture of feldspar, quartz and mica. The majority of gemstones, however, are composed of just one mineral, the main exception being lapis lazuli, which contains a mixture of lazurite, sodalite, calcite and pyrite, and is therefore a rock and not a mineral.

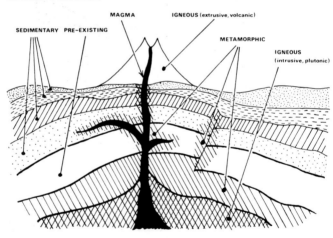

Fig. 1.2. Sketch showing the relative positions of igneous, sedimentary and metamorphic rocks

Rocks and their constituent gem minerals can be divided into three broad groups which indicate the way in which they were formed (*Figure 1.2*). These groups are as follows.

Igneous

This type of rock solidified from the molten magma either within the earth or at its surface. Those rocks which solidified deep inside the earth are called intrusive, plutonic or abyssal rocks (such as granite), while those which were formed by the more rapid cooling of magma at the surface are called extrusive or volcanic (e.g. lava). Most of the important gem minerals,

Fig. 1.3. Single crystals of feldspar, quartz, tourmaline, beryl, topaz and zircon, as formed in intrusive or plutonic rocks

such as the feldspars and quartzs, tourmaline, beryl, topaz and zircon, are found in intrusive or plutonic rocks, the slower rate of cooling making it possible for quite large crystals to form from the molten residues (*Figure 1.3*). As the temperature of the original molten magma dropped, the feldspar minerals were the first to solidify, and having plenty of space they produced large well-shaped crystals. As the magma continued to cool, other minerals crystallised out. Of these, quartz was one of the last to solidify, and as it had much less room than the others in which to grow, was not always able to produce such well-defined crystals.

Fig. 1.4. The sawn and polished section of a geode. Rapid cooling probably produced the main agate layer of microscopic crystals, while a more leisurely fall in temperature allowed time for the larger quartz crystals in the centre to form. The method by which the concentric bands were produced is still a matter of speculation

Many of the intrusive gem bearing rocks formed as coarse-grained granites called *pegmatites*. *Geodes* are another form of igneous occurrence in which gem minerals have been precipitated as crystals in almost spherical cavities formed by molten or aqueous residues trapped in the magma (*Figure 1.4*).

Sedimentary

This group was formed from the fine deposits of sand, grit and clay which were eroded from ancient pre-existing rocks by the action of rain, wind and flowing water to form layers of sandstone or limestone. Except for organic materials such as amber and jet, these rocks contain no primary gem material. However, if the original weathered rock contained heavier minerals (e.g. gem minerals) these were often washed out and swept away to form secondary or alluvial deposits. These gemstones are classified as sedimentary gem material, and can be seen in the gem gravels of Burma and Sri Lanka. Opal is also formed as a secondary deposit, and was washed out of silica-bearing rocks and soils to solidify in fissures and crevices as thin veins of porous silica gel material.

Metamorphic

These are pre-existing igneous or sedimentary rocks which have been subjected to high pressures and temperatures beneath the surface of the earth, and as a result have undergone changes of chemistry and shape. Marble is a metamorphic rock which has been produced in this way from limestone. In one of these metamorphic processes, liquid magmas were forced into cooler rocks causing reactions which produced the gemstone varieties of emerald, alexandrite, ruby and sapphire. Other gem minerals were formed as a result of the large-scale shearing and crushing of rocks. Examples of these are garnet, andalusite, serpentine, nephrite and jadeite.

The manner in which gemstones were produced in nature can therefore be related to the igneous, sedimentary or metamorphic processes of rock formation. A gemstone is normally classified, however, by the type of deposit in which it is found. This is termed the source or occurrence of the gemstone and is either a *primary* or a *secondary* deposit. In primary deposits, gemstones are found at the site where they were originally formed. This type of deposit is of particular interest to the mineralogist and geologist as it provides evidence of the method of gemstone formation. Secondary, or sedimentary, deposits have been carried from the place of their formation either by weathering agents such as wind or rain, or by rivers (when they are called *alluvial* deposits).

Evidence of the distances travelled by sedimentary deposits can be seen in their abraded surfaces (e.g. as in water-torn topaz pebbles or the rounded diamond crystals of the Namibian coastline).

Diamonds (*Figure 1.5*) differ from the rest of the gem minerals in that they were formed much deeper in the earth's crust. It is thought that diamonds crystallised at least 100 miles below the earth's surface from graphite, carbon dioxide or methane at very high temperatures and pressures. The diamond-bearing magma was then driven up to the surface by explosive gas pressure, and solidified to form the present day kimberlite pipes which constitute the world's primary source of diamonds.

Fig. 1.5. Rough diamond crystals. From left to right: a triangular twinned 'macle', a 'shape' (distorted octahedron), a 'stone' (octahedron), and a 'cleavage'. (Photo courtesy of De Beers)

The tops of the pipes are thought to have originally extended above the surface of the earth as hills, or, in the case of the larger pipes, as mountains. Over hundreds of millions of years, these kimberlite hills were eroded by the weathering action of wind and rain into low-lying hillocks or 'kopjes', the diamonds in them being washed away to form secondary deposits along river beds and marine terraces.

The composition and characteristics of gemstones

Fortunately for the gemmologist, whose task it is to identify unknown specimens, gem minerals are in general very different from each other in their physical characteristics. These differences are due mainly to their chemical compositions, which can vary from the simple carbon constituent of diamond to the complex boro-silicate compound of tourmaline.

One of the qualities principally dependent upon the gemstone's chemical composition is its durability. This can best be seen by grouping the gem minerals into the following four chemical categories:

Oxides	These are generally hard and resistant to chemical attack.	
	Chrysoberyl	$BeAl_2O_4$
	Corundum	Al_2O_3
	Opal	$SiO_2.nH_2O$
	Quartz and chalcedony	SiO_2
	Spinel	$MgAl_2O_4$
Carbonates	These are soft and easily attacked by acids.	
	Calcite	$CaCO_3$
	Malachite	$Cu(OH)_2CuCO_3$
	Rhodochrosite	$MnCO_3$
Phosphates	These are soft and not very resistant to acid attack.	
	Apatite	$Ca_5(F,Cl)(PO_4)_3$
	Turquoise	A complex hydrated phosphate of copper and aluminium
Silicates	These are hard and very durable. They represent the majority of gemstones.	
	Beryl	$Be_3Al_2(SiO_3)_6$
	Feldspar	An aluminium silicate in combination with sodium, potassium or calcium.
	Garnet	A silicate of various combinations of magnesium, manganese, iron, calcium, aluminium and chromium

Jadeite	$NaAl(SiO_3)_2$
Nephrite	$Ca_2(Mg,Fe)_5(OH)_2$ $(Si_4O_{11})_2$
Peridot	$(Mg,Fe)_2SiO_4$
Rhodonite	$MnSiO_3$
Topaz	$Al_2(OH,F)_2SiO_4$
Tourmaline	A complex boro-silicate of aluminium and alkalis, with iron, calcium, lithium, magnesium, manganese and potassium
Zircon	$ZrSiO_4$

Groups, species and varieties

Gemstones can also be grouped into *species* and *varieties,* the latter differing from each other only in colour or general appearance. An example of this can be seen in ruby and sapphire which are varieties of the mineral species corundum. Quartz is also a mineral species and contains the varieties amethyst, citrine, smoky quartz and rock crystal. All varieties of the same species have the same chemical composition and crystal structure.

In mineralogy, there are over two thousand different mineral species. As an aid to classification, these are gathered together into a series of *groups*, each of which contains species having similar features or characteristics. In gemmology, however, there are only two sets of gemstone species which have enough in common to qualify as groups. These species comprise the feldspar and garnet gemstones.

It is easy for the student gemmologist to become confused by the apparently alternative names a gemstone may have under the headings of species and varieties (and sometimes groups). To resolve any ambiguity, those gemstones possessing both a variety and a species name are listed in *Table 1.1*, which also shows the relationships in the feldspar and garnet groups.

Table 1.1

Group	Species	Variety
	beryl	emerald, aquamarine, morganite (pink), heliodor (yellow), goshenite (colourless)
	chrysoberyl	chrysoberyl (yellow, greenish-yellow), alexandrite (red in tungsten light, green in daylight), cymophane (greenish-yellow cat's eye)
	corundum	ruby, sapphire (blue, violet, green, yellow, pink, orange, colourless)
feldspar	orthoclase	moonstone, orthoclase (yellow)
	microcline	amazonite (green)
	plagioclase	oligoclase (yellow), labradorite (multi-coloured sheen), sunstone or aventurine (bronze or gold-spangled), albite moonstone
garnet	almandine	(purple/red)
	pyrope	(blood red)
	grossular	hessonite (orange/brown, green and pink) massive grossular (jade green)
	andradite	demantoid (green), topazolite (golden yellow)
	spessartite	orange, yellow, flame red
	uvarovite	emerald green
	opal	white opal, black opal, water opal (colourless with internal iridescence) Mexican fire opal (orange)
	quartz	amethyst, citrine (yellow), rose quartz, rock crystal (colourless), aventurine quartz (green, blue or brown with mica spangles), tiger's eye (yellow/brown), hawk's eye (blue/green), jasper (red/brown)
	chalcedony (crypto-crystalline quartz)	chalcedony (blue/grey unbanded), agate (curved concentric bands), cornelian (red), chrysoprase (green), onyx (straight bands)
	tourmaline	achroite (colourless), indicolite (blue), rubellite (red/pink), schorl (black), tourmaline (green, yellow, brown)

Use of the hand lens and microscope

At the beginning of this chapter, mention was made of the variety of gem testing equipment now available to the gemmologist. Despite the sophistication of these instruments, perhaps the most useful and frequently used of all the gemmologist's 'tools' is the hand lens, or loupe, as it is sometimes called.

The optimum magnification factor for a hand lens is 10×, as this is sufficiently powerful to reveal most of a gemstone's identifying features. Lenses having a magnification of 20× or more are available, but their focus is rather critical and their field of view limited, all of which makes them more difficult to use. Image distortion and colour 'fringing' are problems associated with high magnification lens, and even with a 10× lens this is a design factor which has to be considered.

Fig. 1.6. A selection of hand lenses

For this reason, all high quality loupes, particularly those intended for use in diamond grading, are fitted with compound lenses consisting usually of a three-lens element (*Figure 1.6*). These 'triplet' lenses are corrected for both spherical and chromatic aberration, which are more scientific terms for distortion and colour fringing.

The student gemmologist may at first experience difficulty in maintaining focus when using a hand lens. This is because it is necessary to keep the gemstone, the lens and the head quite steady when looking into the stone. The best technique is to hold the lens close to the eye, steadying the hand holding the lens by resting it against the cheek. The gemstone can then be held (preferably in a pair of tweezers) in the other hand, and positioned for best focus. Wavering of the hand holding the tweezers can be prevented by resting it against the hand holding the lens (*Figure 1.7*). If glasses are worn, the lens should be held in contact with them.

Fig. 1.7. The author demonstrating the method of holding the hand lens and tweezers for maximum steadiness

With all loupes, illumination of the stone under inspection plays an important part. The lamp should be adjusted so as to direct light into the side of the gem, any internal features then appearing brightly lit against a relatively dark background.

When magnification, mechanical stability or illumination become limiting factors, we must turn to the microscope, which for many gemmologists is, in any case, the preferred instrument.

The trend towards binocular microscopes has meant that it is now possible to spend extended periods, without strain, in the inspection of a gemstone. While one of the uses of the microscope is in the classification of gemstones, perhaps its most useful function is to discriminate between synthetic and natural gemstones, and to help in the detection of imitation gems.

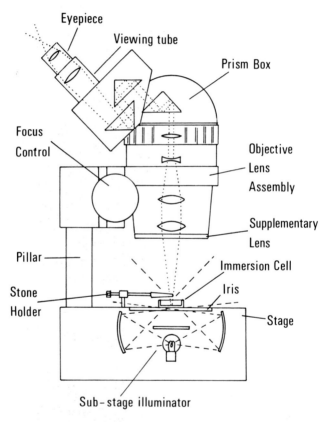

Fig. 1.8. Sketch showing the components and ray path for one half of a typical stereo microscope. The illuminator in the substage assembly is set for dark-field work

The sketch in *Figure 1.8* will serve to identify the components in a standard binocular microscope. The majority of modern instruments are of the binocular type, and these are produced in two basic versions. The simpler type has a single-objective lens system whose image is split and shared by the two eyepieces. The more expensive type is a true stereo version, and has two independent objective lens systems, each one coupled to its own eyepiece.

For gemmological use, the most appropriate magnifications lie in the range 10x to 80x, with most work being done in the region of 15x to 30x. This magnification range can be

Fig. 1.9. A typical stereo zoom microscope designed for gemmological work. The ring-type illuminator can be raised to provide shadowless incident illumination (courtesy Eickhorst & Co.)

covered by the use of interchangeable objective lenses mounted in a 'turret'.

Many microscopes have a zoom lens system which gives a stepless range of magnifications (*Figure 1.9*). While a zoom facility may sound attractive, it is not necessarily always the best choice, as compromises in the design of a zoom lens may result in a performance which is inferior to that of a turret lens system. For comparative work, where dimensions are important, the known fixed magnifications of the multi-objective turret lens may make it preferable to the stepless magnification range of a zoom system.

Apart from the simplest of monocular models, most microscopes are provided with a built-in means of illuminating the specimen on the stage. This can be as basic as a lamp and condenser lens assembly under the stage, with an iris control to vary the area of illumination. In the more sophisticated models, the choice of incident, light-field or dark-field illumination is provided, the latter two being contained in the substage lamp assembly. With light-field illumination, light is transmitted upwards through the specimen and into the objective of the microscope. With dark-field illumination, the light is directed into the gem from the sides, and there is no direct light path between the lamp and the objective. Dark-field illumination is generally the preferred method for gemmological work as it gives better contrast.

To avoid the possibility of lowering the objective onto the specimen when focusing, and thus scratching the lens, it is good practice always to start with the objective just clear of the specimen, and to find the initial focus setting by adjusting the objective away from the specimen. Focusing is more easily carried out by using the lowest magnification power of the microscope and then increasing this as required.

If the microscope is provided with its own light source, this should be set for dark-field illumination. If only light-field illumination is provided, the iris control should be set so that the minimum of light escapes round the sides of the stone. If only external illumination is available, this should be adjusted so that the light is directed into the side of the stone.

When inspecting the interior of a gemstone, particularly when using the higher magnifications, trouble is often experienced because the illuminating light is reflected back from the facets of the stone. Dark-field illumination often overcomes this problem, but if difficulties are experienced with facet reflections, these can be eliminated by placing the gemstone in a glass immersion cell (see *Figure 1.8*) and filling the cell with a liquid having a refractive index near to that of the stone. In practice, the liquid does not have to match the refractive index of the gemstone, and even immersing the stone in water reduces reflections (see Chapter 6).

2 Colour, Lustre and Sheen

In Chapter 1, beauty of appearance was given as the prime quality of a gemstone. In a world where colour is one of the dominant visual sensations, it is not surprising that a gemstone's beauty is largely determined by its colour. Although colour is a common everyday experience, and as such is normally taken for granted, in gemmological work it is important to understand exactly how the effects of colour are produced in a gemstone.

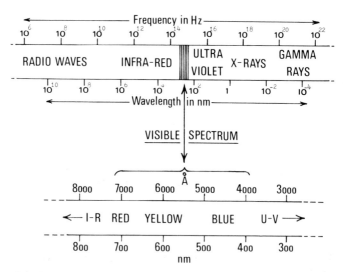

Fig. 2.1. Diagram showing the frequencies and wavelengths in the electromagnetic spectrum. The shaded portion in the middle represents the small visible section

First of all we must take a look at the nature of light itself. Light is a form of energy which is radiated by means of electromagnetic waves. These are similar to the ones generated for radio and television transmissions, but have a very much shorter wavelength. The relative positions occupied by light and radio waves in the electromagnetic spectum can be seen in *Figure 2.1*. Light waves in the visible spectrum are bounded at the long-wavelength red end by infrared heat rays, and at the violet end by ultraviolet rays.

While with radio and television transmissions the wavelengths are measured in metres and centimetres, the wavelengths of light are measured either in *ångström units* (in older textbooks) or in the more recently adopted *nanometre* standard (a nanometre is one millionth of a millimetre, and is equal to ten ångström units).

The relationship between the wavelength of an electromagnetic wave and its frequency is given by the following expressions:

$$\text{Wavelength} = \frac{\text{Velocity of light}}{\text{Frequency}}$$

$$\text{Wavelength in metres} = \frac{300}{\text{Frequency in megahertz}}$$

$$\text{Wavelength in nanometres} = \frac{300 \times 10^9}{\text{Frequency in megahertz}}$$

Selective absorption

White light is composed of an approximately equal mixture of all the colours or wavelengths that make up the visible spectrum. When we look at a coloured gemstone in white light, the colour we see is the result of the absorption by the stone of various wavelengths in the original white light. In a transparent stone, these wavelengths will be absorbed from the light as it passes through the stone; with an opaque stone, the wavelengths will be absorbed as the light is reflected back from the stone's surface.

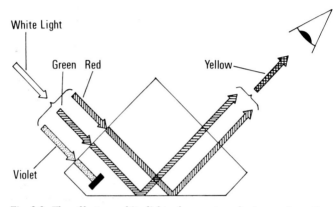

Fig. 2.2. The effect on white light of a gemstone having an absorption band in the violet end of the spectrum

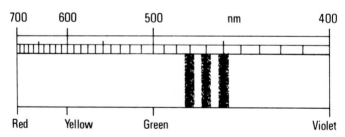

Fig. 2.3. An absorption spectrum showing the three iron bands which are diagnostic for sapphire

If the violet end of the spectrum is absorbed by the gemstone, the colours in the remaining part of the white light will combine together to give the stone a yellow appearance (*Figure 2.2*). If the wavelengths from yellow through to violet are absorbed, the gemstone will appear red.

This suppression of certain wavelengths or colours in white light is called *selective absorption*, and can be made visible by means of an instrument called a spectroscope. Light is passed through the gemstone (or reflected off its surface) and is then directed into the spectroscope where a combination of prisms spreads the light out into a continuous spectrum of colour. The various wavelengths which have been absorbed by the gemstone are visible along the spectrum as a series of dark bands. The result as seen in the spectroscope is called an absorption spectrum, and is often sufficiently distinctive to provide a means of gemstone identification (*Figure 2.3*). A detailed description of the spectroscope and its use is given in Chapter 8.

Allochromatic and idiochromatic gemstones

The selective absorption of light by a gemstone is caused either by impurities present in the gemstone (such as chromium in ruby, or iron in amethyst), or by the chemicals in the stone's composition (e.g. copper in malachite, or manganese in rhodonite). Gemstones whose colours are caused by impurities are called *allochromatic* (i.e. 'other-coloured'), while those which owe their colour to their own chemical composition are called *idiochromatic* (i.e. 'self-coloured').

The majority of coloured gemstones are allochromatic, and some of these also occur as pure colourless varieties. Examples of this can be seen in 'white' sapphire, zircon and topaz, and in the goshenite variety of beryl.

The transition elements

The selective absorption of light in both allochromatic and idiochromatic gems is caused mainly by the presence of what are called *transition* elements. In the allochromatic gems, these act as the colouring impurities, while in the idiochromatic stones they are an integral part of the gem's chemical formula.

The eight metallic transition elements, together with examples of gemstones coloured by them, are as follows:

Vanadium   Blue zoisite, green vanadium beryl, synthetic corundum (alexandrite simulant), blue/violet sapphire.

Chromium Ruby, emerald, alexandrite, red spinel, pyrope garnet, chrome grossular garnet, demantoid garnet, chrome diopside, jadeite, pink topaz.

Iron   Sapphire, sinhalite, peridot, aquamarine, tourmaline, enstatite, amethyst, almandine.

Nickel   Chrysoprase, synthetic green and yellow sapphires.

Manganese Rhodochrosite, rhodonite, spessartite, rose quartz.

Copper   Malachite, turquoise, dioptase, synthetic green sapphire.

Cobalt   Synthetic blue spinel, blue synthetic quartz, cobalt glass. (Cobalt is not found in any natural transparent gemstone.)

Titanium   Blue sapphire.

Note. The transition elements have been arranged here, not in order of their atomic numbers, but so that they can be easily remembered by using a simple mnemonic phrase, 'various colours in nature make completely contrasting tints'.

In some instances, the positions of the absorption bands produced by a transition element can cause the stone's body colour to change when it is moved from one type of lighting to another. This colour change effect is called *metamerism*, and can be seen most strikingly in the rare alexandrite variety of chrysoberyl. In this particular gemstone there is a broad central absorption band in the yellow part of the spectrum, and this causes the stone to appear red in the blue-deficient light of a tungsten lamp, and green in the more balanced spectrum of daylight.

Because of alexandrite's rarity and high price, several simulants have been marketed which attempt to copy this colour change effect. One of these is a synthetic corundum doped with vanadium. The colour change with this simulant is from an amethyst purple in tungsten light to a pale blue in daylight, and therefore makes the stone easily distinguishable from the genuine article. A synthetic spinel simulant has also been marketed, and this approaches more closely to the true alexandrite colours.

In 1977, a true synthetic copy of chrysoberyl was marketed having the correct colour change of best quality Siberian alexandrite. Although this synthetic alexandrite is many times more expensive than the synthetic corundum or spinel versions, it is only a fraction of the cost of the natural gemstone, and presented yet another identification challenge to the gemmologist.

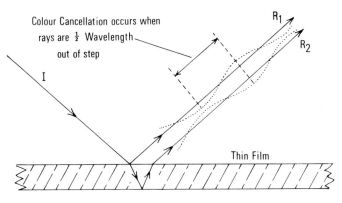

Fig. 2.4. Representation of the production of colour in a thin film by interference between reflected rays. The wavelength or colour related to the extra distance travelled by R_2 is either cancelled where this is equal to half a wavelength (as shown), or reinforced when it is a whole wavelength (i.e. when the two rays are in phase)

Colour effects can also be produced by the *interference* between the rays reflected from a gemstone's surface (*Figure 2.4*). If a ray of white light (I) meets a very thin transparent layer, it will be reflected from the top surface of this layer as well as from the lower surface. Both reflected rays (R_1, R_2) will be parallel with each other, but because the one that penetrated the layer has travelled further, it will be out of step, or out of phase, with the other one.

At a particular colour or wavelength in the reflected light, the two rays will be exactly half a wavelength out of step (and therefore in phase opposition – see *Figure 2.4*), and the colour represented by this wavelength will be cancelled. The remaining components in the reflected light will then combine together to produce the complementary colour (as in selective absorption). Alternatively, if the out-of-step distance is such that the two rays are exactly in step again at a particular wavelength, then this colour will be reinforced, and the reflected light will contain this as its dominant colour. The part that this interference effect plays in the production of colour in precious opal, labradorite and moonstone is explained later in this chapter.

Unlike the majority of gemstones, whose various hues are caused by the presence of the transition elements, colour in diamond is produced by defects inside the crystal lattice. In the yellow-tinted Cape series, these defects are due to dispersed nitrogen atoms which displace some of the carbon atoms in the lattice. Larger numbers of nitrogen atoms produce the colour in the less common green stones, while brown diamonds probably owe their colour to the presence of both nitrogen and amorphous carbon. In natural blue diamonds, the colour-producing defects are caused by the presence of boron atoms.

While the value of a coloured gemstone is influenced by the depth and purity of its colour, the price of diamond is usually determined by the complete absence of colour. The exceptions are the so-called 'fancies', whose shades of yellow, red, pink, orange, brown, green and blue are sufficiently attractive and rare to give them an enhanced value. As diamonds can also be artificially coloured by treatment in an atomic pile, it is possible that the colours in the 'fancy' diamonds are due to lattice defects brought about by natural irradiation in the earth.

Although the colour of a gemstone is probably its most important feature, and certainly has a big influence on its commercial value, it is not often of much use to a gemmologist when it comes to making an identification. There are, of course, the obvious exceptions, such as the bright grass green of peridot, the purple of amethyst and the orange of fire opal.

With the transparent allochromatic gem minerals beryl, corundum, tourmaline and topaz however, colour is much less useful as a distinguishing feature, as these gems crystallise in many different hues. In these stones, the colour depends entirely on which of the transition elements was present at the time the mineral was formed. In the case of tourmaline, crystals are sometimes found in which the colouring impurity changed during the growth of the mineral to produce a prism which changes along its length from blue to green or pink.

Zircon also comes in a variety of colours, although the popular blue and golden brown hues are produced by heat treatment. Like diamond, zircon owes its colour not to the transition elements, but to crystal defects. In zircon this is brought about by the presence of minute quantities of radio-active uranium and thorium. In the so-called 'low' green and brown zircons, alpha-particle bombardment from these elements has almost completely broken down the internal crystalline structure, and the stone is described as a *metamict* zircon. Other properties of the low zircons are also affected by the breakdown in crystalline structure. These include both *refractive index* and *dispersion*, which are appreciably lower in metamict zircons than in normal types (see in Appendix B under 'zircon').

With the possible exception of zircon, which has other easily recognisable optical features, it may be difficult on occasions to distinguish between allochromatic gemstones by appearance alone. In earlier times, before the chemistry and characteristics of gemstones were fully understood, many stones were classified simply by their colour. Evidence of this can be seen in the British Crown Jewels, where the Black Prince and Timur rubies are, in fact, red spinels!

With opaque gemstones, and in particular the idiochromatic species malachite, turquoise, rhodonite and rhodochrosite, colour is a far more distinctive identifying feature. Other opaque gemstones which are easily recognisable by virtue of their colour and their surface patterning are the varieties tiger's eye, aventurine quartz, agate, onyx and amazonite.

The optics of lustre and sheen

There are two further optical qualities which, like colour, contribute to a gemstone's beauty. These are called *lustre* and *sheen*, and are to do with the way in which light rays are reflected from the stone.

The lustre of a gemstone is the optical effect created by the reflectivity of the stone's surface. Lustre is directly related to the quality of the stone's surface polish, and is therefore partly dependent upon the gem's hardness as well as on its internal structure. Because of differences in hardness and other properties, not all gem materials possess the same degree of lustre after polishing. For this reason, various terms have come into use to describe the more distinctive lustres exhibited by various gems. The following list is a selection of the most commonly used of these terms, together with some illustrative examples of gem materials.

Metallic The type of very high lustre associated with metals (e.g. gold, silver, platinum), and seen in some metallic compounds (e.g. pyrites, galena).

Adamantine The high surface polish achieved with diamond, good quality zircons and demantoid garnet.

Vitreous A glass-like lustre typical of the majority of gemstones (e.g. corundum, topaz, quartz).

Resinous The more subdued polish seen in amber.

Waxy The almost matt surface typical of turquoise and jadeite.

Greasy The appearance of polished soapstone and nephrite.

Pearly The lustre seen with mother-of-pearl.

Silky A fibrous lustre typical of satin spar.

These adjectives are only intended as relatively broad descriptions of the surface appearance of a polished stone, but in recent years an instrument called a *reflectivity meter* has made it possible to measure a stone's lustre with some accuracy. Details of this measuring technique, and the way in which it is used in gemstone identification, are given in Chapter 7.

While lustre is the *surface* appearance of a stone in reflected light, sheen is the optical effect created by light rays reflected back from *beneath* the surface of the gemstone. As with lustre, there are several descriptive names which are used to describe the various types of sheen exhibited by gemstones. These names are as follows:

Chatoyancy   This is the 'cat's eye' effect caused by reflection of light from parallel groups of fibres, crystals or channels within the stone (*Figure 2.5*). In the case of pseudocrocidolite, or tiger's eye as it is better known, these channels are the fossilised remains of asbestos fibres which have been replaced by quartz. The finer and more highly reflecting the fibres or channels are, the brighter is the resulting chatoyant 'line'. While many stones are polished as cabochons to reveal this chatoyant effect, the finest quality cat's eye stones occur in the cymophane variety of chrysoberyl.

Asterism   This is a 'star' effect present in some rubies and sapphires (which are usually polished in the cabochon shape to show the effect to best advantage). Like chatoyancy, the effect is due to fine parallel fibres or crystals, but in this case there are three sets of them intersecting each other at 60°.

Although the best asterism occurs in corundum as a six-pointed star, it can also be seen occasionally in rose quartz. In diopside and some garnets it appears as a four-pointed star. In these stones there are only two groups of fibres, and these intersect each other at 90° for garnet, and 73° for diopside. Synthetic star rubies and sapphires have been produced, but with these the star effect tends to be much more prominent than it is in the natural stone.

Iridescence   This is the 'play' of rainbow-coloured light caused by extremely small regular structures beneath the

30

Fig. 2.5. An enlarged view of the parallel quartz channels beneath the surface of a polished piece of tiger's eye. The bright chatoyant lines are running roughly at right-angles to these channels

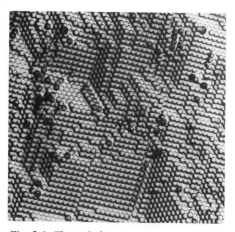

Fig. 2.6. The orderly arrangement of silica gel spheres in opal, as revealed by the electron microscope at a magnification of 25 000×

surface of the gemstone. Like a thin film of oil which produces a sheen of coloured light, these structures 'interfere' with the light reflected from the gemstone, reinforcing some colours and cancelling others (see *Figure 2.4*).

The effect is seen at its best in precious opal, where it is caused by millions of microscopic spheres of silica gel which make up the bulk of the gem. These spheres are all the same size and are arranged in regular rows and patterns (*Figure 2.6*). Because of their identical size and the symmetry of their arrangement, they colour the reflected light by a combination of interference and diffraction effects. This latter effect is produced when white light is split up into its spectral colours by being passed through a narrow aperture, or a series of apertures (as in the optical grating used in the diffraction grating spectroscope — see Chapter 8).

The colours produced by precious opal depend on both the angle of viewing and the diameter of the spheres. An opal containing spheres of 300 nm diameter will reinforce light having a wavelength of up to twice this dimension (i.e. from red to violet), while one with spheres of 200 nm will only reinforce light rays at the blue/violet end of the spectrum. In common or 'potch' opal the spheres are of random size, and there is very little diffraction or reinforcement of the reflected light. This results in a milky white *opalescent* effect which is almost completely lacking in colour.

Labrador-escence   This is a particular form of iridescence which can be seen in the labradorite variety of feldspar and in spectrolite, a beautiful Finnish type of labradorite. In both cases, the effect is caused by thin layers or flakes of feldspar beneath the stone's surface.

Adular-   Also known as 'Schiller', this is the bluish sheen
escence   seen in moonstone. It is another form of iri-
              descence, and is caused by thin laminated plates
              or layers within the stone.

Transparency

The *transparency* of a stone is yet another important optical
quality of a gemstone which affects both its beauty and its
value. The various degrees of transparency, translucency and
opacity are defined as follows:

Transparent   An object viewed through the stone can be seen
                clearly without loss of detail (e.g. diamond, rock
                crystal).
Semi-   The image of an object viewed through the gem
transparent   will be blurred but still recognisable (e.g. moon-
                stone, fire opal).
Translucent   The stone will transmit some light, but objects
                cannot be seen through it (e.g. chrysoprase,
                jadeite).
Semi-   Some light can still penetrate the stone, but only
translucent   through the edges (e.g. turquoise, aventurine
                quartz).
Opaque   The stone is sufficiently dense optically to prevent
                the passage of any light (e.g. malachite, jasper).

The colour of a gemstone also has an effect on its transparency. Deeply coloured stones will pass less light than lightly
coloured ones. Another factor which will effect transparency
is the presence of internal flaws or inclusions. In addition, the
thicker the stone, the greater will be the loss of light passing
through it. For these reasons, a deeply coloured stone polished
in cabochon form is often hollow-cut (i.e. the base is hollowed
out to make the stone thinner, thus improving its transparency
and lightening its colour).

Artificial coloration

Many gemstones are subjected to heat treatment to improve or change their colour. Although in most cases this is a permanent and irreversible process, expensive gems such as sapphires and rubies must be described as 'treated' stones if their colour has been improved in this manner.

Many citrines are produced by the heat treatment of amethyst, and are sometimes described as 'burnt amethyst'. Dark green tourmalines from South West Africa can be changed to a paler emerald shade of green by heating, and pale green beryl can be transformed to a more attractive blue aquamarine colour. The purple tints of blue zoisite can be diluted to produce a blue stone more closely resembling sapphire, and the colour of some sapphires can be lightened and thus improved by the same method. Most Sri Lankan rubies are heat treated to drive out the iron colouring impurity and produce a more attractive pale red shade.

Topaz and zircon are perhaps the best known of all the heat treated gemstones. Brown and yellow topaz from Brazil loses its colour at $500-600\,^{\circ}C$, but on cooling turns pink. If the stones are heated above this temperature they remain colourless on cooling. When brown zircons are heated to $900-1000\,^{\circ}C$ in a reducing atmosphere (i.e. one deficient in oxygen) they usually turn an attractive blue shade. This colour is liable to fade, however, if the stones are exposed to strong sunlight for long periods (the fading occurs more rapidly under long-wavelength ultraviolet light), but the blue colour can be restored by heating the stones in air to a dull red temperature. If brown zircons are heated to $850-900\,^{\circ}C$ in the presence of oxygen (i.e. in air) they usually change to a golden brown or become colourless.

The physical and chemical changes caused by heat treatment are quite complex, and are not fully understood even today. It is probable, however, that in gemstones such as blue sapphire and tourmaline, the process improves the stone's colour by driving out iron. Zircon's colour (like that of diamond) is associated with defects in the crystal lattice, and in this case the application of heat probably results in a partial reforming of the lattice structure.

The other method of colouring gemstones is to dye or stain them, but this cannot be considered as a legitimate and permanent colour change comparable with heat treatment. Cryptocrystalline gem materials have a slightly porous surface and their colour is often improved or changed by the use of chemicals. Agates are stained to increase the contrast in their banding, and a black onyx simulant has been produced by boiling chalcedony in a sugar solution and then treating the stone with sulphuric acid. Jasper has been stained to imitate lapis lazuli, when it is called Swiss or German lapis. White or poorly coloured jadeite has sometimes been stained to simulate the more valuable green variety, and the colour of turquoise has been similarly improved.

While it is very difficult to detect colour improvement or colour change which has been produced by heat treatment, the fact that most stained materials have been coloured to imitate other gem minerals makes them more easily detectable. Those materials which have been stained simply to improve their colour can often be detected by fluorescent or spectroscopic methods.

As already mentioned, diamonds can be artificially coloured by irradiating them with neutrons in an atomic reactor. This produces a homogeneous green body colour, which can be changed to yellow or a cinnamon brown by a subsequent heat treatment at $500-800\,^{\circ}C$. Some rarer types of diamond can be changed to red or purple by this method, though in general it is only the poorer colour yellow 'Capes' whose colour is worth improving. The stones are intensely radioactive after treatment, but this dies away rapidly.

Diamonds were first artificially coloured by irradiation in the early part of this century, when Sir William Crookes used a radium source to turn specimens green. Unlike the more recent neutron-irradiated diamonds, the colour of these stones did not penetrate deeper than the surface, and could therefore be easily polished off. More important, the radium-treated stones were strongly radioactive after treatment. This radioactivity had a very long 'half-life' or decay rate, and this made the stones unsafe for use in jewellery.

A colour change effect can also be produced by means of electron bombardment in an electron accelerator, and with this process some diamonds turn a pale blue or a blue/green. The colour here is only 'skin-deep' however, and can be polished off.

The protons, deuterons and alpha particles generated by a cyclotron can also be used to change the colour of a diamond, the resulting green shade again being only skin deep. Like neutron-irradiated stones, these rapidly lose their initial radioactivity.

In all these irradiation processes, the colour change is a permanent one, and is brought about by producing defects in the diamond's crystal lattice which affect the light passing through the stone. While it is legitimate to improve the colour of a diamond in this way, it is fraudulent to sell it (as a 'fancy') without disclosing that it has been artificially coloured.

The detection of irradiated diamonds is mainly by means of spectroscopic analysis (see Chapter 8), but diamonds which have been turned blue by electron bombardment can be distinguished from natural blue diamonds by testing them for electrical conductivity. Natural blue stones are semiconductors and will pass an electric current, but artificially coloured blue diamonds are electrically non-conducting.

If a diamond has been cyclotron-irradiated through the side of its pavilion, a zone of colour will be apparent near the girdle; if irradiated through the table, a dark ring will be visible on looking at the pavilion side of the stone. If the diamond has been treated through the pavilion at right-angles to the girdle, a scalloped shape will be seen round the culet on looking down through the table.

3 Crystallography, the Science of Crystal Structures

Crystallography plays an important part in both gemmology and mineralogy, and although at first sight it may seem to be a rather academic subject to the student, it has many practical applications in lapidary work, in diamond polishing and in gemstone identification.

All materials, including those used in jewellery, are either *amorphous* or *crystalline* substances. In an amorphous substance, the atoms and molecules are positioned randomly (i.e. they are not linked to each other in any special order or pattern), and because of this they can never have any naturally-occurring characteristic shape. Glass is a common example of an amorphous material, and it has neither a regular molecular structure nor a characteristic external shape. Other examples of amorphous substances are amber, jet and opal.

The majority of gemstones, however, are minerals, and these are all crystalline substances in which the atoms and molecules are aligned in a regular and symmetrical three-dimensional pattern. In most instances, this underlying symmetrical crystal structure makes itself visible in the external shape of the rough mineral specimen. The few gem minerals which, although they are crystalline substances, do not have a naturally-occurring characteristic shape are called *massive*, a term which refers to their lack of identifiable form rather than to their size. A common example of a massive crystalline gem material is rose quartz.

The most important characteristic possessed by a crystalline substance (and absent from an amorphous one) is that its physical properties vary with the orientation of the crystal. With an amorphous material its properties are the same no matter what the direction of measurement, but in a crystalline substance they are related to the directional planes formed by its constituent atoms and molecules.

A striking example of a directional-dependent property can be seen in diamond, which can be cleaved apart in the four directions which are parallel to its octahedral crystal faces, but in no other direction. Hardness in a diamond is another property which varies with direction, a fact which has to be taken into account by the polisher as he facets this hardest of all gem materials.

In addition to cleavage and hardness, optical properties such as colour can also vary with direction in crystalline materials, and these are all factors which are of particular relevance to the lapidary.

So far, we have seen how a knowledge of crystallography can be of help to the diamond polisher who uses it to polish facets in the direction of least hardness, to the cleaver who may be able to save valuable sawing time by rapidly parting the stone in two along a cleavage plane, and to the lapidary who uses his understanding of a gem's optics to bring out its colour to best effect. A further practical application of crystallography is in the identification of unpolished crystal specimens by the recognition of their characteristic shapes or 'habits'. This can be particularly useful when the size or surface condition of the specimen makes it difficult to carry out optical tests.

Elements of symmetry

So far, the adjectives 'regular', 'symmetrical' and 'pattern' have all been used to describe a crystalline substance. In crystallography, the concept of symmetry as applied to the crystal structure is very important. For most gemmological work it is sufficient to be able to recognise the gem crystal habits, and to be aware of their associated optical characteristics. However, the three *elements of symmetry* are fundamental to the study of crystallography, and are defined here for the sake of completeness.

Axis of symmetry

This is an imaginary line positioned so that when the crystal is turned round on it, the characteristic profile of the crystal appears two, three, four or six times during each complete

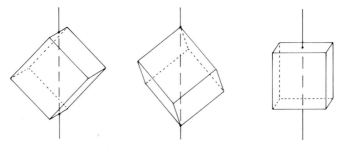

Fig. 3.1. From left to right, examples of two-fold, three-fold and four-fold axes of symmetry in a cubic crystal

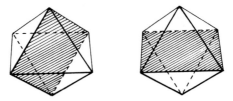

Fig. 3.2. Two of the planes of symmetry in an octahedron

revolution. There are usually several possible axes of symmetry in a crystal, and these are described as two-, three-, four- or six-fold axes, depending on the number of times the crystal profile makes its appearance during a single rotation of the crystal (see *Figure 3.1*).

Plane of symmetry

This is a plane through a crystal which divides the crystal into two mirror-image halves (see *Figure 3.2*). A cube has nine such planes.

Centre of symmetry

A crystal possesses a centre of symmetry when identical faces and edges occur on exactly opposite sides of a central point.

The seven crystal systems

Crystals can be grouped into seven basic *crystal systems*, all of which have different degrees of symmetry. These seven crystal systems are classified in terms of imaginary lines of reference called crystal axes, which pass through the centres of the crystal faces, or edges, to meet at a point inside the crystal called the *origin*. The axes are used, in effect, to indicate the shape of the crystal, and the seven crystal systems are defined in terms of the numbers of these axes, their lengths and the angles between them. The systems are further defined by means of their elements of symmetry. The seven crystal systems with their associated axes and elements of maximum symmetry are as follows.

(1) The cubic system

Crystals in this system have the highest order of symmetry and are sometimes called isometric. The cubic system has three axes, all of which are of equal length and intersect each other at right-angles. There are thirteen axes of symmetry (six two-fold, four three-fold and three four-fold), nine planes of symmetry and a centre of symmetry.

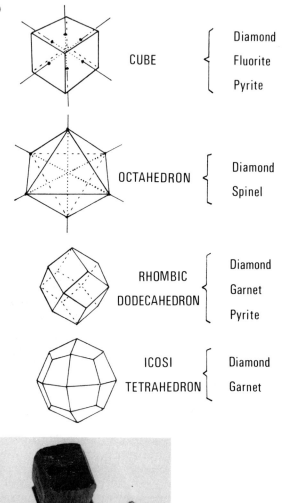

CUBE — Diamond / Fluorite / Pyrite

OCTAHEDRON — Diamond / Spinel

RHOMBIC DODECAHEDRON — Diamond / Garnet / Pyrite

ICOSI TETRAHEDRON — Diamond / Garnet

Fig. 3.3. The cubic system, with examples of pyrite (rear), spinel (left) and fluorspar crystals

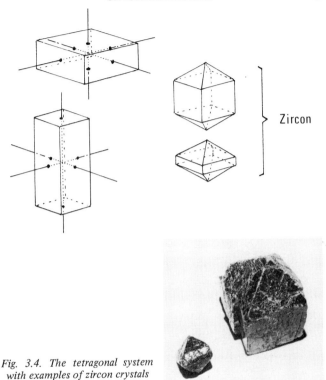

Zircon

*Fig. 3.4. The tetragonal system
with examples of zircon crystals*

Common forms are the cube, the eight-sided octahedron and the twelve-sided dodecahedron (*Figure 3.3*). (Examples: diamond, garnet, spinel.)

(2) The tetragonal system

This has two equal-length axes at right-angles to each other, and a third (principal) axis which is either shorter or longer than the other two, and at right-angles to them. There are five axes of symmetry (four two-fold and one four-fold), five planes of symmetry and a centre of symmetry.

The commonest form is the four-sided prism (*Figure 3.4*). (Examples: zircon, scapolite.)

(3) The hexagonal system

There are four axes in this system, the first three being of equal length and intersecting each other at 60° in the same plane. The fourth (or principal) axis is at right-angles to the others and usually longer. There are seven axes of symmetry (six two-fold and one six-fold), seven planes of symmetry and a centre of symmetry.

The commonest form is the six-sided prism (*Figure 3.5*). (Examples: beryl, apatite.)

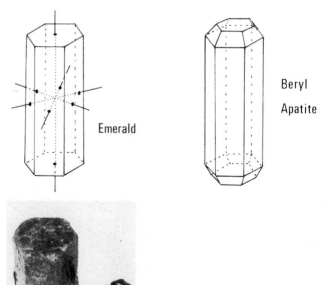

Emerald

Beryl

Apatite

Fig. 3.5. The hexagonal system with examples of apatite (left) and emerald crystals

(4) The trigonal system

This system also has four axes which are arranged in the same manner as in the hexagonal system. The symmetry of the trigonal system is, however, lower than that of the hexagonal system. Full, or *maximum* symmetry, can be seen in the gem mineral benitoite, which has four axes of symmetry (three two-fold and one three-fold), three planes of symmetry and a centre of symmetry.

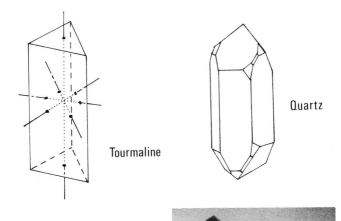

Tourmaline

Quartz

Fig. 3.6. The trigonal system. The examples of quartz (left) and calcite crystals illustrate contrasting habits in the same system. The rhombohedron shape can also be arrived at by cleaving a hexagonal shaped prism of calcite

The bulk of trigonal crystals have what is described as *normal* symmetry, and this consists of one axis of symmetry (three-fold), three planes of symmetry and a centre of symmetry.

Common forms are three-sided and six-sided prisms (*Figure 3.6*). (Examples: quartz, corundum, tourmaline, the latter having *no* centre of symmetry.)

(5) The orthorhombic system

This system has three axes, all at right-angles to each other and all having different lengths. There are three axes of symmetry (all two-fold), three planes of symmetry and a centre of symmetry.

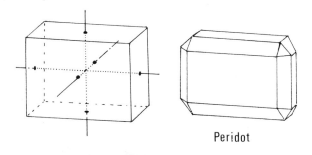

Peridot

Fig. 3.7. The orthorhombic system, with examples of chrysoberyl and topaz crystals. The chrysoberyl crystal on the left is formed from triple interpenetrant twins

Common forms are the four-sided prism and the flattened tabular crystal (*Figure 3.7*). (Examples: topaz, peridot, chrysoberyl.)

(6) The monoclinic system

There are three axes in this system. They are all of different lengths. Two axes are inclined at an angle (other than 90°), and the third one is at right-angles to the other two. There is one axis of symmetry (two-fold), a plane of symmetry and a centre of symmetry.

Common forms are blocky wedge-shaped crystals (*Figure 3.8*). (Examples: moonstone, jadeite, nephrite.)

(7) The triclinic system

This is the least symmetrical of all the seven systems. It has three axes, all of different lengths and all inclined at angles

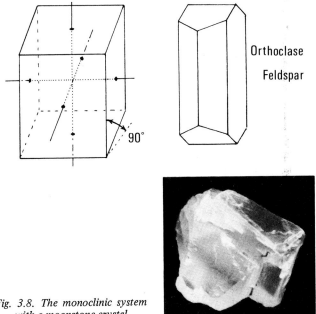

Orthoclase

Feldspar

Fig. 3.8. The monoclinic system with a moonstone crystal

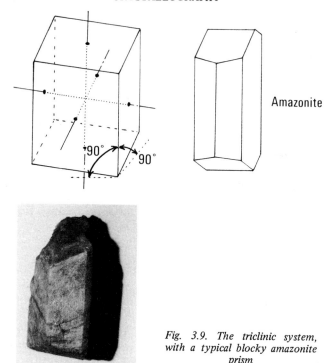

Amazonite

Fig. 3.9. The triclinic system, with a typical blocky amazonite prism

(other than 90°) to each other. There is a centre of symmetry, but no axes or planes of symmetry.

Common forms are blocky wedge-shaped crystals (*Figure 3.9*). (Examples: amazonite, rhodonite, sunstone.)

Identification of rough gem samples by shape

Even from the few examples shown in the illustrations, it is clear that minerals belonging to the same crystal system can often have very different habits, despite the similarity of their internal crystal structures. These differences in habit can be the result of combinations of basic forms within the system.

Other differences are due to the variety of ends, or terminations, which some crystals adopt. Some of the more complicated shapes are caused by the parallel growth or interpenetration of two or more crystals, as can be seen in the chrysoberyl specimen in *Figure 3.7*.

The many differences in crystal habit can be confusing at first to the student, who may have difficulty in associating them with the simple basic shapes of the seven crystal sytems. This very variety can, however, be an advantage, as it often makes the identification of a mineral possible through the individuality of its shape.

One of the best ways of becoming familiar with the habits of gem mineral species is to spend some time examining a well-stocked collection. Such collections exist in many museums, and probably one of the most comprehensive of these is the one on display in the gem mineral hall of the Geological Museum in South Kensington, London. Here, all of the important species and varieties of the various minerals can be seen in both the unpolished and polished states. As a further aid to familiarisation, a set of 35 mm colour slides is available from the Gemmological Association of Great Britain (see page 228 for address). These slides consist of individual diagrams of the crystal systems, each one surrounded by gem mineral specimens illustrating that particular system.

As with most branches of science, crystallography has its own 'language'. This consists of terms which help to describe the various features of a crystal. The following are the most useful ones for gemmological purposes.

Acicular	Slender needle-like crystals.
Botryoidal	Resembing a bunch of grapes (e.g. malachite).
Columnar	A crystalline structure composed of a series of slender prisms. Very fine ones are called *fibrous.*
Contact twins	This is where the twin-halves of a crystal have grown with one half rotated through $180°$ to the other half. In diamonds a contact twin is called a 'macle'. Repeated twinning produces a *lamellar* structure.

Interpenetrant twins	Here, two (or more) crystals have grown in proximity and have penetrated each other. The result is often a cross, star or hexagonal form.
Crystal face	One of a number of flat surfaces bounding a crystal.
Dendritic	A 'branching' or tree-like feature. Often used to describe a type of inclusion (as in moss agate and green tree agate).
Dome	This is a form whose faces intersect the vertical axis and one horizontal axis, but are parallel to the third axis.
Form	This is a group of similar crystal faces.
Isomorphism	Minerals exhibit isomorphism when they have identical external forms but differ chemically (e.g. the garnet group).
Isomorphous replacement	The replacement of one element in a mineral by another element having the same valency which, while maintaining the same form and crystal structure, may cause wide variations in the mineral's physical properties (e.g. the garnets).
Polymorphism	Minerals which differ in external shape but have the same internal composition (e.g. graphite and diamond; andalusite, kyanite and sillimanite).
Lamellar	A crystalline structure composed of straight or curved plates or leaves.
Mamillary	Rounded intersecting contours (e.g. haematite).
Massive	Without crystal form.
Octahedron	Eight-sided crystal (bi-pyramid) in the cubic system.
Dodecahedron	Twelve-sided crystal in the cubic system.
Parallel growth	Unlike twinned crystals, the faces of parallel growth ones have the same orientation.
Pinacoid	This is a pair of crystal faces which are parallel to two crystal axes, and are cut by the third.
	In a *basal pinacoid*, the faces are parallel to the crystal's lateral axes, and often form the

terminating faces of a prism. *Macro* and *brachy* pinacoids are parallel to the crystal's principal axis. The macro pinacoid is cut by the longer (macro) axis, and the brachy pinacoid is cut by the shorter (brachy) axis.

Prism   A crystal form whose faces are parallel to the principal axis and are cut by the lateral axes.

In *first-order* prisms each prism face is cut by two lateral axes; in *second-order* prisms, each face is cut by only a single lateral axis (see *Figures 3.4* and *3.5*).

Pseudomorph   A mineral which has adopted an external form other than its normal habit by copying, for example, the shape of a pre-existing crystal or organic structure.

Scalenohedron   A six-sided bi-pyramid with unequal sides.

Striations   Growth lines on the surface of a crystal.

Tabular   A crystal having a flattened tablet-like habit.

Termination   The crystal form often found at the end of a prism.

Crypto-crystalline gems

Examples of the more common gem minerals and their crystal habits are given in *Table 3.1*. The table includes the gemstone species chalcedony, jadeite, nephrite and turquoise which are classified as *crypto-crystalline*. This type of mineral has grown not as a single large crystal but as an aggregate of small or microscopic crystals (or crystalline fibres) randomly oriented within the body of the gem. For this reason, the habit of crypto-crystalline minerals is always massive, and the gems are mainly semi-translucent or opaque. Some of their other optical properties are also different from normal crystalline minerals and these are described in Chapter 6.

Although the total number of crypto-crystalline minerals may seem small, the number of varieties in the chalcedony species (see list in *Table 1.1*) ensures their frequent appearance

Table 3.1

Gemstone	Crystal system	Habit
apatite	hexagonal	long six-sided prism, often terminated with pyramid (also short prism, tabular and massive)
beryl (emerald, aquamarine)	hexagonal	long six-sided prism, often striated vertically; terminations are rare
calcite	trigonal	rhombic prisms, scalenohedra and six-sided prisms
chalcedony (agate)	trigonal (crypto-crystalline)	massive, botryoidal, mamillary, nodules, geodes
chrysoberyl	orthorhombic	long prismatic crystals; triple interpenetrant twins forming 'hexagon'
corundum (ruby, sapphire)	trigonal	tapering barrel-shaped bipyramid, hexagonal prism
diamond	cubic	octahedron, dodecahedron, icosi tetrahedron (cubes rare), contact twin (macle)
feldspar (moonstone) feldspar (amazonite oligoclase, labradorite)	monoclinic triclinic	crystals of both types resemble each other in habit; both are prismatic and often blocky with wedge-shaped faces
fluorspar	cubic	cube, interpenetrant cubes and octahedral cystals (naturally occurring octahedra are rare, but the cube cleaves readily into this form)
garnet	cubic	deodecahedron, icosi-tetrahedron (and combinations of both)

Table 3.1 *cont.*

Gemstone	Crystal system	Habit
jadeite	monoclinic (crypto-crystalline)	massive
nephrite	monoclinic (crypto-crystalline)	massive
peridot	orthorhombic	tabular
pyrite	cubic	cube, dodecahedron (also massive and granular forms)
quartz	trigonal	six-sided horizontally-striated prism with rhombohedron termin-ations
rhodochrosite	trigonal	massive
rhodonite	triclinic	tabular and massive
rutile	tetragonal	four-sided prism with pyramidal terminations (also acicular and massive granular)
scapolite	tetragonal	four-sided prism (also massive).
spinel	cubic	octahedron and spinel twin (contact twin)
topaz	orthorhombic	flattened four-sided prism with pyramidal or dome termination (prism faces often vertically striated)
turquoise	triclinic (crypto-crystalline)	massive

Table 3.1 *cont.*

Gemstone	Crystal system	Habit
tourmaline	trigonal	triangular prism (generally with rounded faces, heavily striated along length)
zircon	tetragonal	four-sided prism with bi-pyramidal terminations

in jewellery. Because of their micro-crystalline structure, the surfaces of crypto-crystalline gems are slightly porous, and can be stained with various colours. Agates are often stained to produce pleasing and contrasting shades of this banded variety of chalcedony, but pale specimens of jadeite have also been dyed to simulate the higher quality and therefore more valuable green variety of this jade material.

Although all crypto-crystalline minerals are massive in habit because of their internal structure, students of gemmology often fall into the trap of thinking that all massive materials are crypto-crystalline. This mistake sometimes happens when classifying rose quartz, as it is very rarely seen with an identifiable external crystal shape and is also translucent in appearance.

Crystalline materials also possess what are called *optic axes*, whose significance will be discussed further in Chapter 6, which deals with the optics of gem materials. Crystals in the tetragonal, hexagonal and trigonal systems have one optic axis and are called *uniaxial*, while orthorhombic, monoclinic and triclinic crystals have two such axes and are called *biaxial*.

In the same way that a point in three-dimensional space can be defined by means of three sets of coordinates, so the various faces of a crystal can be identified by what are known as crystallographic indices. The most commonly used indices are those devised by the nineteenth century British crystallographer W. H. Miller. These Miller indices consist of three numbers for a three-axes crystal, or four numbers for a four-axes crystal, and enable the orientation in space of a crystal face to be coded unambiguously. For students who are interested in the subject, further details of the Miller index system are given in Appendix B.

The metamict state

Some minerals which have experienced alpha-particle bombardment (either from their surroundings or from radioactive impurities or constituents) have as a consequence lost their original crystalline structures and become amorphous. These minerals are described as *metamict* substances. In 'low' zircon, the metamict state has been brought about by the presence within the gemstone of minute amounts of radioactive uranium and thorium. The rare mineral ekanite which is found in the Sri Lankan gem gravels is also a metamict material and contains a large amount of thorium.

Suppliers of mineral specimens

Brian Lloyd Minerals,
    15a Pall Mall, London SW1Y 5LU
Gregory Bottley & Co.,
    30 Old Church Street, London SW3
R. Holt & Co. Ltd,
    98 Hatton Garden, London EC1
Manchester Minerals,
    420 Manchester Road, Heaton Chapel, Stockport, Cheshire
Roughgems Ltd,
    121–123 Charterhouse Street, London EC1M 6AA
The Gemmological Association of Great Britain,
    St Dunstan's House, Carey Lane, London EC2V 8AB

4 Hardness, Fracture, Cleavage and Parting

In Chapter 1, the prime qualities of a gem material were given as beauty, rarity and hardness. While the beauty or rarity of a gem may qualify it for use in jewellery, its *hardness* or *durability* will, however, be the final deciding factor. This is because a gem must be able to withstand the wear and tear which jewellery is subjected to in everyday use. The biggest factor here is not so much the occasional hard knock which a ring or a bracelet may receive, but rather the universal presence of microscopic particles of quartz in the atmosphere and in household dust. These particles are in continual contact with the gem's surface and act upon it as a fine abrasive grit.

For both gemmological and mineralogical purposes, the hardness of a material is defined as the ability of that material to resist abrasion when a pointed fragment of another substance is drawn across it (provided that the pressure used is insufficient to cause cleavage).

Mohs scale

The scale of hardness which is used universally for gemmology and mineralogy was devised by the German mineralogist Friedrich Mohs. This scale is a comparative one, and is based on the principle that any substance with a given hardness value or number will scratch another substance having a lower number, and will in turn be scratched by one having a higher number.

Friedrich Mohs selected as his standards ten easily obtainable minerals, each having a distinctive hardness. The standards used in the Mohs hardness scale are as follows, and are numbered one to ten in increasing order of hardness:

1	Talc	6	Feldspar
2	Gypsum	7	Quartz
3	Calcite	8	Topaz
4	Fluorspar	9	Corundum
5	Apatite	10	Diamond

Perhaps the most important fact to be remembered when using the Mohs hardness scale is that it is a relative one and not a linear one (i.e. the difference in hardness between each successive number is not the same). For example, the difference in hardness between corundum at 9 and diamond at 10 is very much greater than that between topaz and corundum (on the linear Rosiwal scale of cutting hardness, topaz is 175, corundum is 1000 and diamond is 140 000).

Although hardness as measured on the Mohs scale is a distinctive constant of most gem materials, its use in gemmology as an identifying feature is limited. This is because a hardness test is, in general, a destructive one as it usually results in a permanent scratch or mark on the gem being tested. In many instances, gemstones have similar values of hardness, and the test would not in any case be confirmatory. As there are often more reliable tests which can be made on a gem, a hardness test should be considered only as a last resort, and even then must be carried out with great care, and restricted to the smallest possible scratch on the least noticeable part of the gem. The hardness test is perhaps one of the more dubious heritages from the earlier days of gemmology before other more reliable test techniques had been developed.

There are, however, a few occasions when a hardness test is justifiable. If, for instance, a large carving is being identified and other tests are not practicable, it may be permissible to carry out a scratch test on the base of the carving without detracting from its appearance. Another occasion when a hardness test can be justified is when testing for diamond. Diamond is the only gemstone which will scratch corundum, and in this case the test is confirmatory, and therefore worthwhile. Hardness tests can also be used on rough mineral specimens, particularly where the size or condition of the specimen rules out other tests.

On the Mohs scale, quartz has a hardness of 7, and as dust particles of quartz are largely responsible for the wear and tear of gem-set jewellery, gemstones must have a hardness at least comparable to this if they are to retain their lustre when set in rings, brooches, pendants and bracelets. Gems which have a hardness of 6 or less will tend to lose their surface polish more quickly than harder stones, and may also suffer facet damage from the occasional knock or blow. (Mohs hardness values for all the gem materials are given in the tables of constants in Appendix B.)

The hardness of a gemstone is due in part to its density, and in part to its crystal structure. The importance of structure can be seen with graphite and diamond which are the two crystalline forms of carbon. The atomic layers in graphite are spaced at 0.335 nm intervals, while in diamond the layers are more tightly linked at 0.154 nm intervals, making this the hardest of all naturally-occurring substances. It is interesting to note that the looser bonding between the layers of graphite allows them freedom to slip relative to each other, and it is this characteristic which makes graphite a useful lubricant.

Directional hardness

Some crystalline gem materials also possess directional hardness. Kyanite, for example, has a hardness of 4 in one direction, and at right-angles to this a hardness of 7. Diamond also varies in hardness with direction, the planes of the docahedral faces (formed at the junctions of the octahedral bi-pyramid) being the softest, and the planes parallel to the octahedral faces being the hardest. The difference in hardness between the cube and octahedral directions in diamond can be as great as ten to one.

Changes in crystal growth which produce twinning (as in a diamond macle), will further complicate matters in a mineral possessing directional hardness, and can cause problems when it becomes necessary to saw or polish across the twinning boundaries. All of these factors are related to the crystallography of gemstones and affect the work of both the lapidary and the diamond polisher, who have to be aware of the best directions for sawing and polishing the gemstone crystal.

The fact that diamond, the hardest of all natural substances, can be cut at all depends on its directional hardness properties. Diamond dust, which is used as the cutting abrasive when sawing or polishing diamonds, consists of minute randomly positioned particles of diamond. It is this random orientation of the diamond dust particles which ensures that some of their cutting edges will be in the direction of maximum hardness when they come into contact with the surface being polished or sawn. When the diamond polisher has to position a facet parallel to the octahedral plane of maximum hardness, he will offset this facet by a small angle so as to obtain a working differential between the hardness of the diamond and that of the diamond dust.

Hardness, and the related factors of density and atomic structure, also influences the quality of the lustre that can be produced on the surface of a gemstone. Soft stones can be difficult to polish, and are usually limited in their lustre, while some crypto-crystalline substances such as jadeite have variations in hardness across their surface which gives them a slightly dimpled or orange-peel look when polished. In contrast to this, diamond is one of the supreme gem materials in both the quality of its adamantine lustre and in the flatness obtainable on its polished facets.

Despite its hardness, diamond is not, however, indestructible. In the early days of diamond prospecting in South Africa there were very few people who were experienced enough to identify diamond from other stones. Because of this many prospectors based their test for diamond on the mistaken belief that it was the only mineral which could survive a blow from a sledge-hammer. (This was one of the tests advocated by the Roman philosopher Pliny some 2000 years ago!) As a result, many fine diamonds were destroyed by this most rigorous of all hardness 'tests'. Much less drastic treatment than that can also cause damage to a faceted diamond, as there are certain directions along which a diamond can be parted or *cleaved* without the use of excessive force. It is possible, for instance, for an unlucky knock in the wrong place to damage the vulnerable facet edges of a polished diamond by cleaving off a sliver from its surface. Zircons, although having a hardness of 7.5, also have a brittle quality, and loose stones should not be allowed to rub against each other in a packet, but should be individually wrapped.

The popular belief that a diamond can be identified by its ability to scratch glass ignores the fact that there are several simulants of diamond (e.g. synthetic spinel, topaz, YAG and even quartz) which will also scratch glass. However, if a scratch test is made on glass using diamond in comparison with the harder of its simulants, the mark made by diamond is certainly deeper, and the diamond 'bites' the glass more readily than the softer gems.

It is equally instructive to make a series of scratch tests on a plain glass microscope slide using various pieces of gem mineral, and applying the same pressure for each test. While diamond makes a deep scratch with ease, those made with corundum and topaz become progressively less deep, and when a hardness value is reached which is only one higher than that of the glass, it becomes quite difficult to start the scratch without applying extra pressure. As a very simple means of estimating a gemstone's hardness, a microscope slide can therefore form a useful reference material, and as it is relatively soft is unlikely to harm a gemstone.

Special *hardness pencils* are manufactured for use in scratch tests, and these consist of metal holders in which are mounted pointed fragments of gem minerals. The hardness number of each mineral is embossed in the ends of the pencil.

When using hardness pencils, the gemstone under test should be scratched (preferably in the region of the girdle where a mark will be least visible) starting with the softest pencil and working up the scale until one is reached which just leaves a visible scratch. The hardness of the gem will be somewhere between the hardness of this pencil and the preceding one. The scratch should then be wiped and inspected under a hand lens to check that it is a mark on the surface and not a line of powder from the test point.

As an alternative to the rather risky use of hardness pencils, a gemstone can be tested by drawing its girdle (*not* its facet edges) across the flat surface of a mineral of known hardness. A set of *hardness plates* comprising moonstone (6), quartz (7), synthetic spinel (8), and synthetic corundum (9) can be obtained to order from most lapidaries, and will be adequate for the majority of hardness tests. A polished section of a synthetic corundum boule can also provide a useful confirmatory test plate for diamond.

It must be emphasised, however, that when it becomes necessary to identify a gem by means of a hardness test, extreme caution must be exercised to avoid damaging the stone. This warning applies as much to diamond as it does to the softer gemstones.

So far we have been discussing the inherent strength of a gem material in terms of its ability to resist abrasion. Now we must look at two other inherent characteristics of a gem which have to do with the weakness of its structure.

Characteristic fractures

The way in which a gem breaks (other than by cleavage or parting) is known as *fracture*, and the surface contour of a fracture can sometimes be distinctive enough to constitute a useful identifying feature. When attempting to identify a gemstone, it is therefore often rewarding to examine it under a hand lens or a microscope for signs of characteristic fracture damage. Typical types of fracture, together with examples of gems in which they occur are as follows:

Conchoidal   This is a shell-like fracture consisting of a series of small scalloped rings similar to those found in a sea-shell. Conchoidal fractures can be seen in quartz and the garnets. It is particularly characteristic of glass.

Splintery   This takes the form of long fibrous splinters and can be seen in jadeite, nephrite and ivory.

Smooth   This type of fracture, although not perfectly flat,
or even   shows no signs of identifiable irregularities. Examples of smooth fractures can often be seen in rough diamonds.

Hackly or   This is typical of the broken surface of most rocks,
uneven   and can also be seen in amber.

Cleavage planes

The *cleavage* property of a gemstone can also help in its identification, but it is more often of interest to the lapidary and polisher. Like some forms of hardness, cleavage is a directional property and can therefore only exist in crystalline substances.

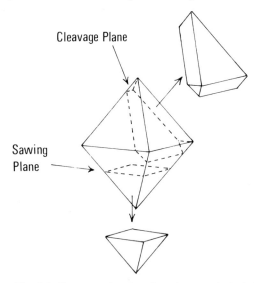

Cleavage Plane

Sawing Plane

Fig. 4.1. Cleavage and sawing planes in an octahedral diamond crystal. There are four directions of cleavage, each one parallel to an octahedron face

A gemstone capable of being cleaved is said to have 'imperfect', 'easy' or 'perfect' cleavage, depending on the ease with which it can be divided or cleaved in two along a plane of weak molecular bonding. Cleavage directions or planes exist in many gem minerals in which the 'adhesion' between the molecular layers is weak, and these layers can be thought of as being analogous to the grain in a piece of wood. All crystalline gemstones have a 'grain', and some of them, like wood, can be worked either by sawing them across the grain or splitting them in two along the line of the grain (*Figure 4.1*). There are also many gemstones, like quartz, which cannot be cleaved at all.

Examples of three gemstones which have perfect cleavage are fluorspar, topaz and enstatite. In fluorspar and topaz, signs of incipient cleavage can usually be seen in the rough crystal. With fluorspar, these cleavage planes appear across the corners of the cube (which can be progressively cleaved to form an octahedron), and in topaz they can be seen at right-angles to the length of the prism. Cleavage is described as being prismatic when it occurs along the major axis of a prism, basal when it is at right-angles to this axis, or octahedral when it is parallel with the faces of the octahedron crystal. When faceting a gemstone having perfect cleavage, the lapidary will avoid the cleavage plane to prevent the stone from parting.

Perhaps the most well known use of cleavage occurs with diamond, where a large irregularly-shaped crystal is sometimes parted by this method rather than by the very slow alternative of sawing. The most dramatic example of this occurred with the 3106 carat Cullinan, which was initially cleaved into three pieces. Before a diamond can be cleaved, however, a groove or 'kerf' must be scratched in the surface of the diamond, parallel to one of the four octahedral cleavage planes. The groove is made with a fragment of pointed diamond cemented in the end of a stick (or, more recently, with a laser beam).

A cleaver's blade is then inserted in this groove, the radius of the blade edge being such that it presses outwards against the sides of the groove like a wedge (*Figure 4.2*). The blade is given a sharp tap, and provided the cleavage plane has been correctly identified, the diamond will split cleanly in two. With smaller

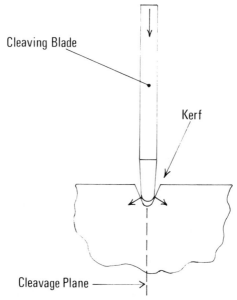

Fig. 4.2. Showing the technique used to cleave a diamond. The tip of the cleaving blade operates as a wedge

and more symmetrical diamonds, the cleavage planes are hardly ever in a direction which would result in the best yield of polished diamonds. In these cases, the diamonds are sawn in two in a direction parallel to the natural girdle of the crystal.

False cleavage or parting

Pseudo-cleavage, false cleavage or *parting* often occurs in gem minerals which, while they do not possess cleavage planes, have a direction of weakness called a parting plane. Parting is usually caused by secondary or lamellar twinning of the gemstone crystal, and occurs in minerals such as ruby and labradorite. It is thought to be due to high pressures which have resulted in thin plates being formed within the stone, these plates having a definite alignment to the crystalline structure.

5 Specific Gravity

Archimedes' Principle, formulated by the Greek scientist, mathematician and philosopher over two-thousand years ago, states that a body immersed in a fluid experiences an upward force equal to the weight of the fluid it displaces. It was this concept which provided the first foolproof method of testing gold for purity of content, and has since become the basis of one of the most important test techniques in gemmology.

Before we look at the various ways in which Archimedes' Principle has been adapted for gemmological work, we must define the terms *specific gravity* (sometimes called *relative density* when referring to liquids) and *density*, so that there can be no confusion between the two.

The *specific gravity* of a substance is the ratio of its mass to the mass of an identical volume of pure water at $4\,^{\circ}$C. As it is expressed as a ratio, no units of measurement are necessary. The specific gravity (SG) of diamond, for example, is 3.52. Water is chosen as the standard for comparative measurement because it is both stable and universally available. By definition, the specific gravity of water is 1.0.

The *density* of a substance is defined as its mass per unit volume, and is measured not as a ratio but in terms of units of mass and volume. The international SI units chosen for density measurement are the kilogram and the cubic metre. Kilograms per cubic metre are expressed mathematically as kg/m^3. Using these units, the density of diamond is $3520\,kg/m^3$.

For gemmological work, however, we are principally concerned with the specific gravity of a substance. As this is a reliable constant for the majority of gem materials, it can be very useful as a means of identifying an unknown specimen, and even when a specimen cannot be positively identified in this way, its SG can still be of value in narrowing down the number of possibilities (SG values of the main gem mineral species are included in the tables of constants in Appendix B).

The SG of a substance is dependent in part on the atomic weights of its constituent elements, and in part on the compactness of the structure formed by these elements. Diamond, for example, with its relatively light but compactly arranged atoms of carbon, has a higher SG than quartz, which is composed of heavier but more dispersed atoms of silica and oxygen.

When handling gemstones it soon becomes evident that with stones of similar size, some feel appreciably heavier than others. Zircon is twice as heavy as an opal of the same dimensions. This method of sensing a gemstone's SG is, of course, very rough and ready, but it is sometimes of value when making a quick subjective assessment of a stone.

Displacement method of SG determination

As a gem material's SG is determined by the ratio of its mass to the mass of an identical volume of water, the measurement of its SG would seem at first sight to involve the calculation of the stone's volume, and, unless this was a simple and regular geometric shape, such a calculation could present difficulties. Archimedes also faced this same problem. His solution was to use the specimen under test to displace its own volume of water into a measuring vessel. To achieve this he designed an apparatus called an *eureka can*. This type of device is still in use today, and consists of a metal container fitted with an overflow pipe.

To measure the SG of a specimen, the eureka can is first filled with water until it just begins to flow out of the pipe. When the water has stabilised and the overflow ceased, an empty beaker is placed under the pipe, and the specimen being measured is gently lowered into the can. The volume of water which is displaced into the beaker then represents the volume of the specimen. The displaced water can then either be weighed, or its volume can be measured in a vessel graduated in cubic centimetres (one cubic centimetre of pure water weighs exactly one gram at $4\,^{\circ}C$, the temperature at which its density is at a maximum). The specific gravity of the specimen can then be calculated by dividing the volume (or weight) of the displaced water into the weight of the specimen:

$$SG = \frac{\text{Weight of gemstone (in grams)}}{\text{Weight of displaced water (in grams)}}$$

or

$$SG = \frac{\text{Weight of gemstone (in grams)}}{\text{Volume of displaced water (in cubic centimetres)}}$$

Although the displacement method of determining specific gravity is suitable for large objects (such as carvings, ornaments or rough mineral specimens), it is not accurate enough for use with gemstones because of their comparatively small volume. However, three other methods, which are all based on Archimedes' Principle, are frequently used in gemmological work.

Hydrostatic weighing

As this method relies on very accurate weighing, it should only be attempted on a beam balance of the analytical type having a sensitivity in the order of ± 0.001 carat (± 0.0002 gram). Top pan balances, which sacrifice sensitivity for convenience, are not normally suitable for hydrostatic weighing because of their lower sensitivity and less adaptable construction.

The hydrostatic method is based on the principle that an object fully immersed in a fluid experiences an upward force, or buoyancy, equal to the weight of the displaced fluid. The method consists of weighing the gemstone in air, and then again when it is fully immersed in pure water:

$$\text{SG of gemstone} = \frac{\text{Weight in air}}{\text{Apparent loss of weight in water}}$$

$$= \frac{\text{Weight in air}}{(\text{Weight in air}) - (\text{weight in water})}$$

This can be expressed in the simple equation

$$\text{SG} = \frac{A}{A - B}$$

where

A = Weight of gemstone in air
B = Weight of gemstone in water

As the method depends on very small differences in weight measurements, the sensitivity of the balance limits the application of hydrostatic weighing to stones of two carats and upwards. Conversely, when weighing large objects, such as carvings, it is not practical to use a beam balance. However, an approximation of SG can still be obtained by using a spring balance to weigh the object in air, and then when immersed in a suitable container of water. With care, even the difference between the jade minerals nephrite at 3.0 and jadeite at 3.3 can be determined by this means.

When using the hydrostatic method, a few balance accessories are necessary (see *Figure 5.1*). First of all, a beaker of distilled or purified water is required, and this must be positioned above the balance's weighpan by using, for example, a wooden platform to span the pan without touching it. A spiral wire support for suspending the gemstone in the water is also needed, and this can be fabricated from a piece of 20−22 s.w.g. copper wire. The spiral stone holder can then be attached by a thin cord to the weighpan hanger.

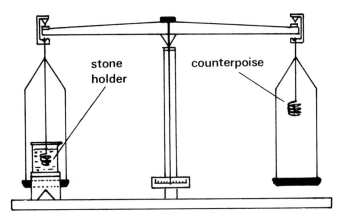

Fig. 5.1. Diagram showing the use of a beam balance for the hydrostatic measurement of specific gravity

The cord supporting the wire spiral should be of fine-gauge mono-filament nylon, and *not* nylon-braided glass yarn or woven cord, as these will absorb water by capillary action. Its length should be adjusted so that the wire spiral remains immersed in the water throughout the vertical swing of the balance. Alternatively, the suspending cord can be dispensed with, and the wire forming the spiral extended so that it can be attached directly to the weighpan hanger (this may, however, reduce the sensitivity of the balance by affecting its free swing).

Finally, to simplify the SG calculations, a counterpoise can be fitted to the other weighpan to balance the weight of the stone support when it is immersed in the water. This can be made up from a longer piece of similar wire, which can then be cut back until the beam is in balance.

The four accessories required for hydrostatic weighing can be purchased from the Gem Instruments Corporation and consist of a beaker, a beaker support, a gemstone holder and a counterpoise. Similar accessories are made by Sauter (*Figure 5.2*), Sartorius and Mettler for use with their substitutional type analytical balances.

Although specific gravity measurements, by definition, should be made with pure water at 4 °C, errors introduced by using purified or distilled water at room temperature will mainly affect the third decimal place in the results, and can therefore be disregarded for normal gemmological work. Of more importance are the possible errors introduced by air

Fig. 5.2. A kit of accessories for the determination of specific gravity by hydrostatic weighing (fitted to a Sauter balance)

bubbles adhering to the gemstone, and by the surface tension of the water, the latter causing a friction-like drag on the wire stone support as it moves through the water.

Bubbles can be removed by thoroughly wetting the gemstone before immersion. Any residual bubbles can then be carefully removed from the stone and the wire support by means of a fine paint brush. The use of distilled water will prevent bubbles forming from air contained in the water. Surface tension effects can be reduced by mixing a drop of detergent with the water. Alternatively, the water in the beaker can be replaced with a liquid having a lower surface tension, such as toluene, and the resulting SG determination multipled by the SG of the liquid (0.869 for toluene). However, as the SG of toluene is much more sensitive to temperature than is water, it is important in this case to make a correction for room temperature when this departs significantly from $15\,^{\circ}$C (i.e. the temperature at which toluene's SG is quoted). A table giving SGs for toluene over a range of temperatures is included in R. Webster's *Gemmologists' Compendium*.

As the successful hydrostatic determination of SG depends on accurate weighing, this is a good place to describe the recommended method for using a twin-pan beam balance. Either gram or metric carat weights are suitable for gemmological work. (There are five metric carats to the gram, and one thousand grams to the kilogram. See Appendix B for other units.) A gram set of weights will usually span the range from 100 down to 1 gram in brass weights, and from 0.5 down to 0.001 gram in aluminium weights.

When making a weighing, a single weight should be chosen which is just heavier than the object being weighed. This is then substituted for an equivalent value of smaller weights which are removed from the pan in turn, working through the weight range until the object being weighed is just heavier than the weights. The lowest value weight which was removed is then replaced on the pan by an equivalent value of smaller weights and the process repeated, working down methodically through the subdivisions until a balance is reached. The weights on the balance pan can then be totalled to arrive at the weight of the specimen. To avoid damaging the balance pivots, it is important to bring the balance to rest before removing or adding weights to the pan. The weights should be handled with tweezers to prevent contaminating them and thus affecting their accuracy. When using a modern substitional type analytical balance, the weight handling is done mechanically, but the method of working systematically through the weight ranges remains the same.

Before leaving the subject of hydrostatic weighing, mention should be made of the Hanneman specific gravity balance, which enables a direct SG measurement to be made without the need for calculation. The balance consists of a long light-weight aluminium beam which is suspended from its centre by a thread. The gemstone is weighed in air in a pan suspended from one end of the beam, and the beam balanced by adding weights to a 'hanger'. The weighing is then repeated with the gemstone immersed in water, and the beam is brought back into balance by sliding the weight hanger towards the fulcrum of the beam. The SG of the gemstone is then read off a scale on the beam at the weight hanger suspension point.

Heavy liquids

One of the alternative (though less precise) ways of determining a gemstone's specific gravity involves the use of heavy liquids. This technique does, however, have two advantages: it is usually quicker, and there is no lower size limit to its use.

In its simplest form, the SG test uses three or four liquids having specific gravities between 2.65 and 4.15. The gemstone under test is immersed in each liquid in turn, its specific gravity lying between the SG of the liquid in which it just sinks and that of the liquid in which it just floats. The principle in use here is again that of Archimedes. If the gemstone being tested becomes freely suspended within one of the heavy liquids, this indicates that it is experiencing an upward force (due to dis-placement of the liquid) which is exactly equal to its own weight. Its SG is therefore exactly equal to that of the liquid.

Heavy liquids were first put to serious gemmological use in the 1920's in the Gem Testing Laboratory of the London Chamber of Commerce, where they were used to separate the denser Japanese cultured pearls from the naturally formed oriental variety. While a variety of heavy liquids have been experimented with over the years, two of these, *bromoform* and *methylene iodide*, have come into general use because of their relative stability and safety. A third heavy liquid, *Clerici's solution*, although both poisonous and corrosive, is also used occasionally for high SG determinations. The compositions and specific gravities of these three liquids are as follows:

Bromoform, $CHBr_3$	2.89
Methylene iodide, CH_2I_2	3.32
Clerici's solution,*	4.15

These three basic heavy liquids can be diluted to produce further test liquids having SGs equal to those of some of the important gemstone species (e.g. quartz at 2.65, and tourmaline at 3.05 — see *Figure 5.3*). This enables the rapid and accurate

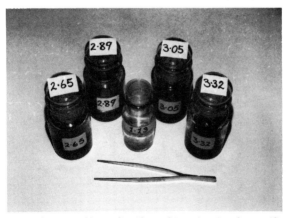

Fig. 5.3. A set of heavy liquids used in estimating the specific gravity of gemstones. The bottle in the centre contains a salt solution used for testing amber

* Thallium malonate and thallium formate in water.

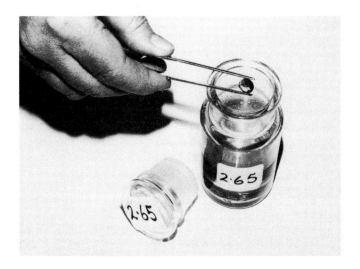

Fig. 5.4. Top: an unknown gemstone specimen being dropped into a bottle of heavy liquid having an SG of 2.65. Bottom: the unknown gemstone floats freely within the liquid, confirming that it is one of the quartz varieties

identification of these gemstones, which float freely within the liquid (*Figure 5.4*). Even where a gemstone sinks in one of the liquids, its rate of sinking will give some indication of how much denser it is than the liquid. When testing small stones, it is important to push them beneath the surface, as the effects of surface tension can sometimes cause a stone to float even when its SG is greater than that of the liquid.

Bromoform and methylene iodide can both be diluted with monobromonaphthalene ($C_{10}H_7Br$) which has an SG of 1.49. Clerici's solution can be diluted with water. When blending heavy liquids to intermediate values, a piece of the appropriate gem mineral should be placed in the bottle (or test tube) to act as an indicator, and the dilutant added in small doses, mixing the liquids thoroughly between each step, until the indicator is in free suspension.

Over a period of time, the diluted solution may become more dense because of evaporation. To give warning of this condition, it is good practice to leave a small piece of indicator mineral permanently in the liquid. When choosing a gem mineral for use as an indicator, the specimen should be free from inclusions, and for this reason it is best to select transparent samples. Ideally, the specimen should be of a simple composition chemically, so that its SG is more likely to be a reliable constant (e.g. fluorspar, quartz, calcite and corundum).

As an alternative to using pieces of gem mineral for SG indicators, specially calibrated glass discs can be employed. A set of twenty-one such indicators, covering the range 2.28 to 4.05, is made by Rayner and is available from Gemmological Instruments Ltd (*Figure 5.5*).

A more precise method of determining a gemstone's specific gravity with heavy liquids is to use a *specific gravity bottle* (*Figure 5.6*). First of all, the approximate SG of the stone is obtained by testing it in the calibrated solutions. Next, a separate heavy liquid is made up to this approximate SG, and carefully adjusted by further blending until the stone becomes freely suspended in it. The exact SG of the blended liquid (and therefore that of the stone) is found by using the SG bottle.

The bottle consists of a small glass phial having a ground glass stopper through which runs a capillary channel. The bottle, in essence, is a precisely calibrated container, and usually has its internal volume (measured at 20 °C) engraved on the outside of the glass. If the bottle is first weighed empty, and then when filled with the unknown heavy liquid (the capillary channel in the stopper ensuring a precise 'fill'), the difference in these two weighings will give the weight of the heavy liquid. If this

Fig. 5.5. A box of twenty-one glass specific gravity indicators ranging from 2.28 to 4.05. The indicators have their SG values indelibly fused into them and can easily be read when immersed. (Gemmological Instruments Ltd – see page 77)

weight is divided by the internal volume of the bottle in millilitres (cubic centimetres) this will give the specific gravity of the liquid and of the gemstone under test.

Specific gravity bottles (listed as 'density bottles') are available from Baird and Tatlock and from Wood Brothers Glass Co. Ltd, in 10, 25, 50 and 100 millilitre sizes (see page 77 for addresses).

Fig. 5.6. A 'density bottle' for the precise determination of specific gravity using blended heavy liquids (Baird and Tatlock)

Because of the nature of the heavy liquids, they should never be used for testing porous stones such as opal and turquoise. Neither is it advisable to immerse a cracked or flawed stone in any of the liquids, as these may enter the stone and cause temporary discoloration.

When testing a stone it is convenient to use a pair of tweezers to insert the stone in the liquid and to retrieve it. To avoid contaminating the liquids it is important that both the tweezers and the stone are cleaned thoroughly between each test. If Clerici's solution is used, both the stone and the tweezers must be rinsed in water after the test.

Safety precautions

Care should be taken not to get any Clerici's solution on the skin or clothes, as it is both poisonous and corrosive. It is also advisable to avoid unnecessary contact with any of the other heavy liquids, as their strong-smelling and slightly toxic vapours can take some time to disperse.

The following note on safety, published in the April 1979 issue of the *Journal of Gemmology*, contains advice from the Health and Safety Executive of the Department of Health and Social Security on the use of gemmological test liquids.

Care should be taken when using ethylene dibromide (a suspect carcinogenic liquid sometimes used for SG determinations and in hydrostatic weighing), *or any other heavy liquids used in gemmology, to avoid skin contact or inhalation of vapour. On no account should any of the liquids used by gemmologists for gem testing be swallowed. In case of contact with the skin, the liquid should be washed off; if in the eyes, they should be well flushed out with running water; if swallowed, vomiting should be attempted and medical assistance obtained.*

As with certain other volatile liquids, it is also advisable to avoid smoking when using heavy liquids.

If methylene iodide is left exposed to daylight, it will slowly darken in colour owing to the liberation of iodine within the solution. However, the addition of a few pieces of copper wire to the bottle will absorb the iodine and lighten the colour of the liquid again. Bromoform also darkens when exposed to daylight, but in this case the discoloration is due to the liberation of bromine. The liquid can be lightened by adding a small quantity of mercury to it and shaking the bottle vigorously.

The mercury will absorb the bromine, and the bromoform can be recovered by decanting it.

Testing for amber

An additional 'heavy' liquid, as suggested by R. Webster, can be used for testing amber and separating it from its simulants. The test liquid consists of a solution made up from ten level teaspoons of common salt dissolved in a half-pint of water. The resulting liquid has a sufficiently high SG to cause amber (SG = 1.08) to float, and the various plastic and Bakelite simulants to sink (copal resins and polystyrene, unfortunately, cannot be separated from amber by this test).

Suppliers of SG test equipment

Baird and Tatlock (London) Ltd,
    PO Box 1, Romford RM1 1HA, Essex
Gem Instruments Corporation,
    1660 Stewart Street, PO Box 2147, Santa Monica, California 90406, USA
Gemmological Instruments Ltd,
    St Dunstan's House, Carey Lane, London EC2V 8AB
Hanneman Lapidary Specialties,
    PO Box 2453, Castro Valley, California 94546, USA
Wood Brothers Glass Co. Ltd,
    Borough Flint Glass Works, Barnsley, South Yorkshire S71 1HL

6 Refractive Index and Double Refraction

For identification purposes, the most important single item of information about a gemstone is its *refractive index*. The reason for this is that the refractive index (RI) of most gemstones is a constant which can be measured with precision to four significant figures (i.e. to three decimal places). Because of this precision and constancy, most gems can be distinguished with ease even when their RIs differ only very slightly (e.g. natural and synthetic spinel; pink topaz and tourmaline).

The refractive index of a material is a measure of the degree by which it bends or refracts light rays passing through it. When a ray of light passes from one medium (such as air) into another medium of greater optical density (such as a gemstone), the ray is refracted, or bent, towards the *normal* (i.e. towards an imaginary line drawn at right-angles to the surface – see *Figure 6.1*). Conversely, when the ray leaves the gemstone and passes into air, it is refracted away from the normal. (*Note*: for optical work all ray angles are given relative to the normal.)

Perhaps the most commonplace example of refraction is the apparent bending of a rod when it is partially immersed in water. The refractive index of a material can, in fact, be expressed as the ratio of the optical density of the material, to that of air (the standard for all practical gemmological purposes):

$$RI = \frac{\text{Optical density of material}}{\text{Optical density of air}}$$

The greater the difference in the optical densities of the two media, the greater will be the amount of refraction of light passing through them. As the velocity of light is decreased in an optically dense material (and is inversely porportional to the optical density), the RI of the material can also be expressed as the ratio of the velocity of light in air to the velocity of light in the medium.

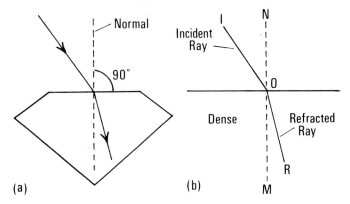

Fig. 6.1. At (a) an incident light ray entering a gemstone from air is refracted towards the normal. A ray leaving the gemstone and passing into air will be refracted away from normal. The general case is shown in (b), where the refractive index of an optically dense material in a less dense medium (such as air) can be calculated by dividing the sine of angle ION by the sine of angle MOR

In 1621, W. Snell, a professor at Leyden University, discovered the *law of refraction*, and made possible the subsequent rapid advances in applied optics. Snell's Law states that:

(1) *When a ray of light passes from one medium into another, there exists a definite ratio between the sines of the angle of incidence and the angle of refraction, which is dependent only on the two media and the wavelength of the light.*

(2) *The incident ray, the normal (at the point of incidence) and the refracted ray are all in the same plane.*

From Snell's Law, the refractive index of a material can therefore also be expressed as the relationship between the angle of incidence in air and the angle of refraction in the material (*Figure 6.1(b)*).

$$RI = \frac{\text{Sine ION}}{\text{Sine MOR}}$$

Fortunately for the busy gemmologist, there are several methods of determining a gem's RI without the necessity of measuring angles and referring to trigonometrical tables.

Approximation of RI by immersion

When a colourless transparent gemstone is immersed in a liquid having an RI close to that of the gem, it virtually disappears. Even if the gemstone has a body colour, its facet outlines (or its shape) will become indistinct. This provides a simple method of approximating a stone's RI, as the gem can be inserted in turn in a series of small pots or dishes containing liquids having various refractive indices. The RI of the stone will be near to that of the liquid in which the stone's outline appears most hazy. As with SG determinations using heavy liquids, this method should not be used with gemstones having a porous surface (i.e. opal and turquoise), or with substances which might be soluble in the test liquid! Suitable immersion fluids and their refractive indices are as follows:

Water	1.33	Bromoform*	1.59
Alcohol	1.36	Iodobenzene	1.62
Petrol	1.45	Monobromonaphthalene	1.66
Benzine	1.50	Idonaphthalene	1.70
Clove oil	1.54	Methylene iodide*	1.74
		Refractometer contact fluid 1.81	

* Heavy liquids used for SG tests (see safety note at end of Chapter 5).

Approximation of RI using Becke line method

Although this technique was originally developed for the measurement of powdered samples of unknown materials (or inclusions), it was adapted by R. K. Mitchell for use with faceted gemstones. The method requires the use of a microscope having light-field illumination (i.e. transmitted light), an iris adjustment and a magnification factor of between 30× and 40×.

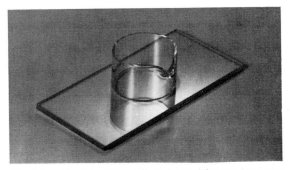

Fig. 6.2. A glass immersion cell can be used for approximating a gemstone's refractive index by the Becke line method. (Gemmological Instruments Ltd.)

The gemstone under test is placed, table facet down, in an immersion cell (*Figure 6.2*) containing a liquid of known RI. The immersion cell is placed on the microscope stage so that the pavilion edges are visible, and the iris control is closed so that the light path is restricted to the area of the gemstone.

The microscope is then focused down from the liquid into the body of the stone. If the facet edges change in appearance from *light* to *dark* as the microscope is focused into the stone, then the RI of the gemstone is *greater* than that of the liquid. However, if the opposite occurs, and the facet edges change from dark to light, then the RI of the stone is less than that of the liquid. By progressively changing the liquid in the immersion cell for one of a higher or lower RI, a close approximation to the gemstone's RI can be obtained. In some cases the SG of the gemstone will be less than that of the test fluid, and it will be necessary to submerge the stone while making the test.

Direct method of RI measurement

This method can only be used on a transparent gem, and depends on the use of a microscope having a calibrated focus adjustment or a vernier height scale (alternatively a dial gauge can be fitted to the microscope). The microscope is first used to measure the apparent depth of the gemstone under test, and is then used to measure its real depth. The refractive index of the stone can then be calculated by dividing the *real depth* by the *apparent depth* (in a doubly-refracting gemstone this will be the RI due to the *ordinary* ray – see under 'Double refraction and its measurement' later in this chapter).

Measurement of a gem's RI using the direct method is limited to an accuracy of plus or minus one per cent, but has the advantage that it can be used to determine the refractive index of high RI stones such as diamond (2.42) and zircon (1.93). Unlike other techniques described later in this chapter, it is also independent of the quality and flatness of the stone's surface finish.

When using the method, the gemstone is positioned on the microscope with its *culet* (see Figure 7.11) in contact with the stage, and its table facet uppermost and parallel with the stage (a small piece of plasticine can be used to secure the stone in this position). Using maximum magnification (to obtain a shallow depth of focus), the microscope is carefully focused on the surface of the table facet, and the position of the focus setting read from the scale. The microscope is then focused down through the stone until the culet is sharply defined, and a second reading is taken. If the second reading is subtracted from the first, the result will be the *apparent depth* of the gemstone.

The *real depth* can be arrived at by moving the stone to one side and focusing the microscope on the surface of the stage. If this third reading is subtracted from the first, the result will be the real depth of the stone (alternatively, this can be measured separately with a Leveridge gauge). The RI of the stone can then be obtained by dividing the real depth by the apparent depth.

For students who do not possess a calibrated microscope, an alternative instrument, devised by H. Bartman, can be produced reasonably cheaply by modifying a vernier calliper gauge (*Figure 6.3*). The modification consists of mounting a hand lens (having at least a 10× magnification) to the top moveable section of the gauge, and fitting a suitable clip to hold the stone or ring shank to the body of the gauge.

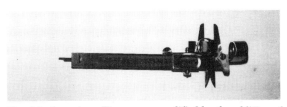

Fig. 6.3. A vernier calliper gauge, modified by the addition of a hand lens and a mounting clip, can be used to measure a gem's refractive index by the direct method

The gauge is first used conventionally to measure the true depth of the stone from table facet to culet. The stone is then fitted in the clip, table facet uppermost, and the gauge adjusted until first the table facet and then the culet is in focus. The readings for these two settings are read off the vernier scale and subtracted from each other to obtain the apparent depth of the stone. As with the microscope method, the stone's RI is equal to the real depth divided by the apparent depth.

Measurement of RI using a refractometer

The *critical angle refractometer* is perhaps one of the gemmo-logist's most important gem identification instruments. To understand its operation, we must first consider what happens when rays of light travelling in an optically dense medium meet the surface of a less dense or rare medium (*Figure 6.4*). If we take ray I_1, which is inclined at a large angle to the normal, this will be reflected back *totally* from the interface of the two

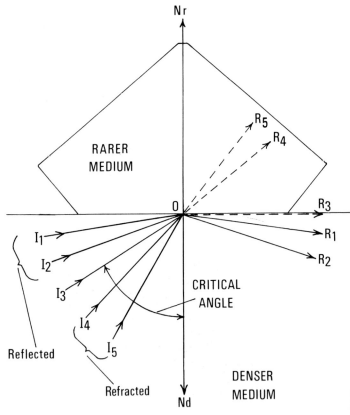

Fig. 6.4. The critical angle of total reflection is dependent upon the refractive indices of both media. At angles greater than the critical (I_3ONd), the incident light rays are reflected. At angles less than the critical angle, the rays are refracted through the rarer medium

media as R_1, and will obey the *Law of Reflection* (i.e. the angle of incidence will equal the angle of reflection, and both the incident ray, the normal at the point of incidence and the reflected ray will lie in the same plane).

As the angle of incidence is progessively reduced (I_2), the ray will continue to be reflected (R_2), but a point will eventually be reached (I_3) where the ray will no longer obey the law of reflection but will travel along the interface between the two media (R_3). The angle at which this occurs is called the *critical angle of total reflection*, and is dependent upon the RI of both the rare and the dense medium. (In lapidary work and diamond faceting, the *critical angle* of a gemstone — relative to air — is of prime importance, and its calculation and practical application will be discussed more fully in the next chapter.)

Fig. 6.5. A standard critical angle refractometer with contact fluid and polarising filter. (Gemmological Association of All Japan)

Finally, the bulk of the light in rays I_4, I_5, having an angle to the normal which is less than the critical angle, will pass into the rarer medium and obey the laws of *refraction*, and only a portion of this light will be reflected back from the interface.

If the dense medium forms part of an optical instrument (as in a refractometer — *Figure 6.5*), and the rarer medium is a gemstone, the rays of light passing through the denser medium will be reflected back from the surface of the gemstone over an arc of incident angles greater than the critical angle, but will 'escape' through the gemstone at angles of incidence equal to or less than the critical angle. As previously mentioned, the critical angle is dependent on the refractive indices of the two media:

$$\text{Sine of critical angle} = \frac{\text{RI of rarer medium}}{\text{RI of denser medium}}$$

As the RI of the denser medium is part of the optical instrument, it is therefore a constant. The RI of the rarer medium in *Figure 6.4* (i.e. the gemstone) is therefore directly related to the critical angle:

$$RI = n_1 \sin I_3 ONd$$

where n_1 is the RI of the dense medium (i.e. the refractometer 'glass'), and $I_3 ONd$ is the critical angle.

The greater the gemstone's RI, the greater will be the critical angle between it and the denser medium.

The critical angle refractometer consists basically of a glass hemisphere or prism, an optical viewing system and a translucent calibrated scale (*Figure 6.6*). Those light rays which have an angle of incidence greater than the critical angle are reflected back at the interface between the gemstone and the glass, and enter the optical system. Rays having an angle less than the critical angle are refracted out into the gemstone. The rays which are reflected are made to illuminate the translucent scale. This results in the scale having a brightly lit section (reflected rays), and a dark section (rays refracted out through the gemstone). The shadow line between the two sections acts as a cursor to indicate the RI of the gemstone on the calibrated scale.

Because of the difficulty in obtaining a good optical contact between the gemstone facet and the refractometer glass, use is made of a *contact fluid*. A drop of this fluid is placed on the centre of the glass and the gemstone is lowered onto it. The fluid effectively excludes any air from the gem/glass interface,

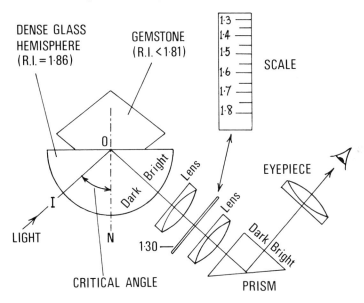

Fig. 6.6. Components and ray path for the critical angle refractometer

and because of its high RI (1.81) it does not interfere with the gemstone readings (a faint shadow edge, caused by the fluid, can be seen at 1.81 on the scale and should not be confused with the gemstone shadow line). The contact fluid consists of a saturated solution of sulphur in methylene iodide plus tetraiodethylene.

There are two main disadvantages with the standard critical angle refractometer. One is that the top end of its range is limited by the RI of both the refractometer glass and the contact fluid. For this reason gemstones whose refractive indices are above 1.81 do not produce a shadow line on the refractometer and are said to have a 'negative reading'. To achieve the highest possible RI range the refractometer prism is made from a glass whose high lead-oxide content raises its RI to 1.86. Unfortunately, this type of glass is relatively soft, and this is the cause of the instrument's second disadvantage, the susceptibility of its prism to scratches. Because of this, care must be taken to avoid damaging the prism's surface when testing gemstones. Even the application of the contact fluid must be made carefully, particularly if this is done with a glass dropper. Such a dropper should only be brought close enough to the glass to transfer a small drop of the liquid, and should not be allowed to touch the glass. The dropper provided with Rayner contact fluid has a flexible plastic end section to safeguard the glass.

The amount of fluid placed on the glass should be limited to a drop 2–3 mm in diameter. When the test is completed, this must be removed carefully from the glass (and from the gemstone) using a soft tissue. If the fluid is allowed to dry on the glass it will tarnish its surface.

To prevent any deterioration in the performance of the refractometer, stains on the glass should be carefully removed with methylene iodide. If this fails to remove them, the glass should be polished gently with jeweller's rouge. If the instrument is not going to be used for a long period, it is good practice to apply a thin film of Vaseline to the surface of the glass.

Because the refractive index of a material varies with the wavelength (or colour) of the light, RI values for gemstones are quoted in terms of yellow sodium light (which has a wavelength of 589.3 nm). Sodium light is chosen because it is a bright and easily reproducible monochromatic illuminant. If red light is used this produces a lower RI reading. Blue light produces a higher reading.

When using the refractometer, it is necessary to provide a source of illumination. If this source is polychromatic (i.e. a filament lamp, or daylight), then the refractometer shadow edge will be less distinct, and will consist of a band of prismatic colours (due to differences in light dispersion between the glass prism and the gemstone). Because the refractive index for gemstones is defined in terms of yellow monochromatic light, readings must be taken at the yellow/green boundary in the coloured shadow edge when using a white light source. Alternatively, all but the yellow portion of this shadow edge can be removed by fitting a deep yellow filter in front of the refractometer eyepiece.

For accurate work, it is best to use a monochromatic yellow light source. Unfortunately, a sodium discharge lamp unit costs even more than a refractometer, and some manufacturers compromise by providing a strong white light source fitted with a narrow-band yellow filter (such as an interference filter). As these lamps dissipate much more heat than a sodium light source, it is good practice to switch them off during periods when the refractometer is not being used, to avoid overheating and subsequent damage to the lamp socket.

The range of refractive indices met with in gemmology extends from 1.43 for fluorspar, to 3.08 for haematite. (RIs of the majority of gemstones are given in the tables in Appendix B.)

Double refraction and its measurement

Light passing through an amorphous (i.e. non-crystalline) material, such as amber or glass, or through a gemstone belonging to the *cubic* crystal system, will obey Snell's Law of refraction and will produce a single refracted ray, regardless of the direction in which the ray enters the gem. Such gems and materials are called *isotropic*, and are singly-refractive.

However, when a ray enters a gem mineral belonging to one of the other six crystal systems (i.e. tetragonal, hexagonal, trigonal, orthorhombic, monoclinic or triclinic), it is split into two rays which are polarised at right-angles to each other. These two rays are called the *ordinary ray* and the *extraordinary ray*, and they travel through the gem at different velocities. Because of this difference in velocity, the two rays are refracted by different amounts.

Gems which cause light to split into two polarised rays are called *doubly-refractive, birefringent* or *anisotropic*. Such gems have *two* refractive indices, and these can be seen on the refractometer as two separate shadow lines.

As polarised light plays an important part in gemmological work, it is worthwhile to digress at this point and consider the phenomenon of polarisation. With ordinary unpolarised light, the rays vibrate in all directions at right-angles to the line of transmission. With *plane polarised* light, the rays only vibrate in one direction, or plane, at right-angles to the line of transmission.

Polarised light can be produced by passing unpolarised light through a polarising filter, which only allows those light rays to pass which are vibrating in the same plane as the transmission plane of the filter. Conversely, the two plane polarised rays emerging from a doubly-refracting gemstone can be separated for individual viewing by interposing a suitably orientated polarising filter (see under 'The polariscope' for descriptions of filter types).

Fig. 6.7. The double image of an ink line reveals the large birefringence of this rhomb of Iceland spar

The amount and type of double refraction possessed by a gemstone is a valuable identification feature. The size of a gem's double refraction (DR) is obtained simply by subtracting the RI of the lowest ray from that of the highest ray. Stones having a high DR, such as zircon (0.058), can usually be identified by the obvious double image of the pavilion facet edges when these are viewed through the table facet with a hand lens. The visual effect of strong birefringence can be seen even more clearly in the Iceland spar variety of calcite (DR = 0.165) which produces a pronounced double image (*Figure 6.7*).

Optical character and optic sign

Anisotropic (doubly-refracting) gemstones possess either one (uniaxial) or two (biaxial) directions along which light is not doubly-refracted. These directions of single refraction in an otherwise doubly-refracting stone are called optical axes, and can be identified with an instrument called a *konoscope* (see under 'The polariscope').

The descriptions *isotropic, uniaxial* and *biaxial* are used to define a gemstone's *optical character*. Both amorphous materials and crystalline substances can be grouped under these three headings of optical character as follows:

Isotropic	Cubic and amorphous
Uniaxial	Tetragonal, hexagonal, trigonal
Biaxial	Orthorhombic, monoclinic, triclinic

This provides us with yet another aid to gemstone identification. Those gems which belong to the *uniaxial* group show a fixed refractive index for the ordinary ray, while their refractive index for the extraordinary ray varies with the angle of entry of the incident ray (i.e. with the rotation of the gemstone on the refractometer glass). In those gems belonging to the *biaxial* group, the RIs of *both* rays vary as the angle of entry of the incident ray is varied. Depending on the way in which the two shadow lines on the refractometer move relative to each other, the gemstones can be further identified as having a *positive* or *negative* optic sign. The method of identifying the optical character and optic sign of a doubly-refracting gemstone will be described in the following paragraphs.

Using the critical angle refractometer

Once the refractometer and the source of illumination are set up ready for use, and the stone to be tested has been thoroughly cleaned, a small drop of contact fluid should be placed in the centre of the refractometer glass, and the stone lowered, table facet down, onto it. It may be necessary, while viewing the shadow edge, to move the stone carefully across the face of the glass in order to get the clearest result. If the stone is doubly-refractive, it will also be necessary to rotate the stone to observe the maximum separation of the resulting twin shadow edges. As it is only too easy to scratch the surface of the glass during these operations, a Rotagem attachment was designed by Rayners for use with their instruments. This device facilitates the rotation of the gem in a controlled manner.

The twin shadow edges of a doubly-refracting gemstone can normally be seen quite easily, but occasionally, where the difference between the two refractive indices is small, the separate edges may be more difficult to determine. In these circumstances, a polarising filter attachment can be fitted over the eyepiece. The rotation of the filter will permit first one shadow edge and then the other to be perceived, and even if these are close together, the alternate appearance and disappearance of the individual edges can be detected.

If, as the stone is rotated on the refractometer, one shadow edge (due to the 'ordinary' ray) remains stationary, while the other (due to the 'extraordinary' ray) moves away to a position of maximum separation, and then returns, the stone can be identified as being doubly-refractive (birefringent), and its optical character as being uniaxial.

If the moving shadow edge has a higher RI reading than the fixed one, the stone is optically *positive,* and if it has a lower RI, it is optically *negative.*

If, however, two shadow edges are visible, and they *both* move as the stone is rotated, this identifies the stone's optical character as biaxial. If the higher-reading edge moves more than halfway from its highest-reading position towards the lowest-reading position of the other edge, the stone is optically *positive*. If the lower-reading edge moves more than halfway towards the higher edge, the stone is optically *negative*.

Variations of these conditions occur depending on the orientation between the optic axes and the facet (e.g. if the optic axis of a uniaxial stone is perpendicular to the facet, the extraordinary-ray shadow edge will remain fixed at full DR).

Distant vision method

While it is practical to measure the RI of any faceted gemstone within the range of the refractometer (provided that a flat facet face of reasonable size is accessible), a problem exists if the stone has very small facets, or has been fashioned into the rounded cabochon form. To overcome this problem, Mr. L. B. Benson, Jr, devised a technique which is called the 'distant vision' method in the UK, and the 'spot' method of the USA.

The method varies slightly with the types of refractometer, but for the Rayner models consists first of coupling the rounded surface of the cabochon to the refractometer glass with the smallest possible spot of contact fluid. This is done by placing a drop of the fluid on a flat surface, and then lightly touching the drop with the surface of the cabochon, which will then pick up the minimum quantity required. The cabochon is then placed on the refractometer glass with its spot of fluid acting as an optical coupler.

The refractometer scale is then viewed with the eye positioned in line with the eyepiece, but $12-18$ in $(30-45$ cm) away from it. By careful positioning of the line of sight, it should be possible to see (superimposed on the limited section of scale now visible) a small 'bubble', which is the spot of liquid coupling the cabochon to the glass. If the line of vision is now moved slowly up and down, the bubble will be seen to change from dark to light. When it is dark, the bubble will correspond to a scale reading below the RI of the stone, and when it is light, the scale reading will be higher than the RI of the stone.

If the line of vision is carefully adjusted until the bubble is divided exactly into two halves (one light and one dark) this will correspond to the scale reading for the RI of the stone. Unfortunately, when the eye is focused for best observation of the bubble, the scale is out of focus, and some mental dexterity is required to hold the bubble in its bisected position and to read the RI from the scale. The Dialdex refractometer (*Figure 6.8*) solves this problem by eliminating the scale.

Special refractometer versions

Two variants of the standard high-density glass refractometer (which are now no longer produced) were devised by Anderson and Payne. One variant replaced the refractometer glass with spinel giving a more open scale between 1.3 and 1.68. The main reason for using spinel was that its dispersion more nearly matched that of the majority of gemstones, and this gave a sharper shadow edge in white light than does the standard version. The other variant used blende (with an RI of 2.37) in place of the glass to extend the high-reading end of the scale.

A third variant made use of diamond (with an RI of 2.42) to extend its range. The diamond-table refractometer was also proposed by Anderson and Payne, and a diamond prism (using abutting glass prisms to transmit the incident and reflected light) was fashioned for the first experimental refractometer from a 6.632 carat 'Silver Cape' stone donated by the Diamond Corporation. The weight of the finished prism was 2.505 carats.

A number of diamond-table refractometers have been made to order, the typical diamond prism dimensions being 7.5 mm × 3.67 mm × 4.2 mm deep with a weight of 1.54 carats. With this instrument, refractive index readings can be taken from 1.55 to 2.03, enabling the RI of zircon, the garnets and sphene to be measured. Perhaps even more important than the wide RI range are the other advantages that diamond offers, i.e. its greater optical purity, its hardness (which enables it to take a much higher polish) and its ability to resist abrasion.

Because of the high dispersion of blende and diamond, it was necessary to use a sodium light with both versions.

Unfortunately, to take advantage of the extended RI range, the contact fluid must have a similarly high RI, and this involves the use of unpleasant fluids such as West's solution (with an RI of 2.05). This consists of an 8:1:1 mixture of yellow phosphorus and sulphur in methylene iodide. Because of the presence of phosphorus in the mixture, it is spontaneously combustible, and therefore must be handled with care.

Fig. 6.8. The Rayner 'Dialdex' refractometer. Instead of a scale marked in RI values, this instrument uses a calibrated control knob to align a black band with the projected shadow line. (Gemmological Instruments Ltd.)

The *Dialdex* refractometer (*Figure 6.8*) is the latest development of the Model S Rayner instrument. It uses a dense-glass truncated prism (in place of the hemisphere shown in *Figure 6.6*) and has a large aperture at the rear for the injection of light from an external source. A hinged cover is provided which, when closed over the gem being tested, excludes all extraneous light. The RI range covered is 1.40 to 1.81; a pull-out eyepiece is provided for focusing.

The main difference between the Dialdex and the earlier Rayner model is, as its name implies, the provision of a calibrated dial on the right-hand side of the instrument. When measuring the RI of a gemstone, this dial, which is coupled to a sliding-ribbon type straight edge, is rotated to make the straight edge coincide with the shadow edge on the scale. The RI reading is then read from the calibrated dial.

This method of reading the RI has the advantage of allowing the user to concentrate on the position of the shadow edge without having to read (and then remember) a scale position at the same time. The RI value set on the dial can then be evaluated at leisure, and readings to an accuracy of 0.001 can easily be estimated. The instrument is provided with both a yellow and a polarising eyepiece filter.

The table spectrometer

Also called a *goniometer*, the table spectrometer (*Figure 6.9*) consists of a fixed collimator (for producing a narrow beam of parallel light rays from a monochromatic source), a table (for supporting the specimen), and a radially-mounted telescope viewer having an eyepiece fitted with cross wires. The position

Fig. 6.9. A Lang table spectrometer (Krüss)

of the telescope, relative to the collimator, can be read off a scale on the table by means of a vernier scale. For gemmological purposes, the table spectrometer is particularly useful for measuring the RI of gemstones which are above the range of the critical angle refractometer.

Provided that the gemstone has suitable facets, which can serve as the two faces of a prism, its refractive index can be determined to better than three places of decimals. This is done by first measuring the angle between the two facet faces, and then measuring the angle of minimum deviation of the 'prism'. As long as the angle between the prism faces is not greater than twice the critical angle for the gemstone, there is no upper limit to the refractive index that can be measured.

The angle between the two selected prism facets is measured as follows. First adjust the collimator for as fine a slit as possible by focusing it on the telescope cross wires. Then position the gemstone in the centre of the table so that its prism facet edges are exactly vertical, and so that the light from the collimator falls upon the adjacent faces of the prism whose angle is to be measured. Turn the telescope round until the image of the collimator slit, reflected from one of the faces of the prism, is centred in the telescope cross wires. Take the reading of the telescope vernier (V). Then turn the telescope to view the image which is reflected from the other prism face, and again record the reading of the telescope vernier (W). The prism angle (A) is equal to half the difference between the two vernier readings:

$$A = \frac{V - W}{2}$$

To measure the prism's angle of minimum deviation, first remove the gemstone from the table and take a direct vernier reading (X) of the slit of the collimator as seen through the telescope. Replace the gem on the table so that it receives the light from the collimator on only one of its prism faces. This light will be refracted by the prism and the telescope should be positioned to receive the refracted image. The slit will in fact be dispersed into a spectrum, and the cross wires of the telescope can be aligned on the yellow part of this spectrum.

The next operation is to find an angular position for the prism that will result in the smallest angle of deviation between the incident light from the collimator and the refracted light picked up by the telescope. To do this, look through the telescope, and rotate the gem about its vertical axis so that the refracted spectrum moves towards the line of incident light emerging from the collimator; follow this image round by rotating the telescope. A point will be reached where the image will appear to stop and then to reverse its direction. In the position where the image stops, adjust the telescope position so that the cross wires again coincide with the yellow section of the spectrum. Read the telescope vernier (Y).

The angle of minimum deviation is obtained by subtracting the direct reading X from the refracted image reading Y:

$$\text{Angle of minimum deviation} = X - Y = B$$

The refractive index for the gem is then;

$$\text{RI} = \frac{\text{sine } [(A + B)/2]}{\text{sine } (A/2)}$$

Because there is usually only one suitable orientation of the gemstone on the spectrometer table, it is only normally possible to obtain a correct RI for the ordinary ray of uniaxial gem minerals. With biaxial gem minerals the RI reading may be anywhere between that of the ordinary and extraordinary rays, as these both vary with orientation. For isotropic minerals of course no such problem exists.

The polariscope

Although the critical angle refractometer is unsurpassed in its ability to reveal and measure single and double refraction in a gemstone, it is sometimes sufficient simply to know that a stone is isotropic or anisotropic. For this uncomplicated diagnostic test the polariscope (*Figure 6.10*) comes into its own.

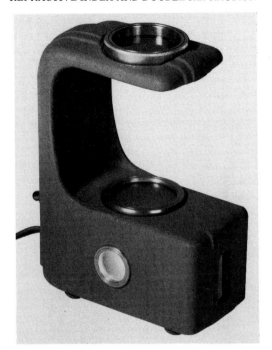

Fig. 6.10. The 'Illuminator' polariscope uses two polarising filters fixed in the extinction position. The aperture at the front can be used to provide a white light source for a refractometer (Gem Instruments Corporation)

There are several versions of the instrument, but most of them use the following three basic components:

(1) A light source (usually built-in).
(2) A protected polarising filter over the light source (which also acts as a test platform for the gemstone).
(3) A second polarising filter through which the stone is viewed.

The gemstone is placed on the lower filter (which is protected from damage by a glass cover plate), and the top filter is rotated into the 'crossed' position where the plane polarised light from the bottom filter is blocked or 'extinguished' by the top filter. If the stone is rotated through $360°$, and is a doubly-refracting gem, it will show four distinct positions (at $90°$ intervals) where it will transmit light (i.e. it will 'rotate' the plane polarised light from the lower filter through $90°$ so that it passes through the top filter). If the stone remains dark when rotated, it will either be an amorphous or an isotropic (cubic) material.

However, it is still possible that the stone could in fact be birefringent, and yet remain dark when rotated. This would happen if the stone was positioned so that the plane polarised light passed through it in a direction which was parallel to an optical axis. For this reason, a stone should be examined in at least two directions before deciding that it is singly-refracting.

Singly-refracting gems, such as diamond, glass and synthetic spinel, occasionally show some indication of birefringence when tested on the polariscope. When this happens, it is never as clearly defined as the four-fold change in light transmission seen in a doubly-refracting stone. It is called 'anomalous double refraction', and is caused by internal strain in the gemstone.

Note: *The anomalous double refraction seen in glass or 'paste' gems is usually quite distinctive, and appears as a strong cross-pattern of dark lines.*

If a crypto-crystalline substance (e.g. chalcedony) is placed on the polariscope and rotated, it will appear uniformly bright in any position. This is due to the random orientation of the many minute crystals of which the gemstone is composed.

Polariscopes use relatively inexpensive plastic polarising sheet, but, before this material was available, *Nicol prisms* were used to produce polarised light. A Nicol prism comprises two sections of optically clear calcite (Iceland spar) which are cemented together with Canada balsam. Light entering the prism is split into two plane polarised rays. The refractive index of the balsam layer is such that it causes total reflection of the 'ordinary' polarised ray, while allowing the 'extra-ordinary' ray to pass through. Plastic polarising sheet contains myriads of microscopic crystals which transmit light with minimum absorption only when it is vibrating in one plane, and are optically opaque to rays which are polarised at right-angles to this plane.

The konoscope

This is basically a polariscope to which has been added a spherical converging lens. This lens is positioned between the polarising filters and enables the optical axis of doubly-refracting stones to be located by means of the interference patterns viewed through the top filter. The instrument is mainly used by gemstone cutters, and is a valuable aid in deciding the best faceting direction for a stone.

Searching for the optical axis in a gemstone requires some practice, and this is best acquired by first experimenting with a rose quartz cabochon, which should be slowly rotated between thumb and forefinger about 15 mm below the lens. The optical character of rose quartz is uniaxial, and the resulting cruciform-shaped interference pattern (as viewed through the top polarising filter) is more easily detectable than the biaxial pattern. When the pattern is located, the optical axis lies in the centre of the concentric interference rings and is in line with the polarised light path.

Instrument developments

Improved versions of gem testing instruments are continually under development. Examples of this are the Krüss *Riplus*, the *Brewster-angle* and the *air-boundary* refractometers. The Riplus uses a strontium titanate prism to achieve a range of $1.75-2.21$. The coupling medium is a paste which becomes fluid at $40\,^{\circ}C$ on the electrically heated prism. The Brewster-angle refracto-meter uses the fact that light reflected from a surface becomes polarised when it is at 90° to the refracted ray. The air-boundary model compares a stone's pavilion/girdle angle with its total internal reflection of light to estimate refractive index.

7 The Optics of Polished Gemstones

In Chapter 6 we saw that a doubly-refracting gemstone is able to split the light passing through it into two separate rays, which are polarised at right-angles to each other. In some *coloured* doubly-refracting stones, these two rays (which are travelling at different speeds in the gem) may emerge differing in shade or colour. When this happens the rays are said to have experienced *differential selective absorption* in the gemstone (i.e. a different portion of the visible spectrum has been absorbed from each ray). The effect is called *pleochroism*, and when the light passing through the stone is split into *two* colours or shades, the stone is said to be *dichroic*; if *three* colours or shades are produced, the gem is *trichroic*. Dichroism is associated with coloured uniaxial stones, and trichroism with coloured biaxial stones.

With some gemstones, such as andalusite and zoisite, pleochroism is an attractive quality, and the stones are cut to bring out all the colours to best advantage. In ruby and blue sapphire, however, one of the dichroic colours is weaker and less attractive than the other, and the stone is cut so that this ray is not visible through the crown facets.

The following stones all possess varying amounts of pleochroism (the first colour listed, in italics, is the body colour of the gem).

Alexandrite	Strong	*Green*, yellowish, pink (in daylight)
		Red, yellowish-red, green (in tungsten light)
Amethyst	Weak	*Purple*, reddish-purple
Andalusite	Strong	*Green*, yellow, red

Apatite	Strong	*Blue*, colourless
Aquamarine	Medium	*Blue*, colourless
Citrine	Weak	*Yellow*, pale yellow
Emerald	Medium	*Green*, yellowish-green
Enstatite	Medium	*Green*, yellowish-green
Heliodor	Weak	*Pale yellow*, pale bluish-green
Hiddenite	Strong	*Green*, yellowish-green, bluish-green
Iolite	Strong	*Pale blue*, dark blue, pale yellow
Kornerupine	Strong	*Green*, yellow, brown
Kunzite	Strong	*Pink*, purple, colourless
Morganite	Medium	*Pink*, bluish-pink
Peridot	Medium	*Green*, yellowish-green
Ruby	Strong	*Deep red*, yellowish-pink
Sapphire	Medium	*Blue*, pale greenish-blue (none in yellow sapphire; in other colours, second ray has yellowish tinge)
Sinhalite	Strong	*Green*, yellow, brown
Sphene	Strong	*Yellow*, reddish-yellow, colourless *Green*, colourless
Topaz	Medium	*Yellow*, two shades of yellow *Blue*, pale pink, colourless *Pink*, pale pink, colourless
Tourmaline	Strong	Two shades of body colour
Zoisite	Strong	*Blue*, purple, brown
Zircon	Weak (except in blue)	Two shades of body colour

With the exception of a few stones which possess strong pleochroism (i.e. andalusite, iolite, ruby, blue sapphire, sphene and zoisite), it may not be easy to detect the presence of dichroic or trichroic colours with the unaided eye. As pleochroism can often be a useful identifying feature in a gemstone, an instrument called a dichroscope was invented to separate the polarised rays, and enable them to be compared side-by-side for signs of colour or shade difference.

The dichroscope (*Figure 7.1*) consists of a cleavage rhomb of optically pure calcite (Iceland spar), which is mounted in a tube having an eyepiece at one end and a square aperture at the other. A glass prism is cemented to each end of the calcite rhomb to allow the light from the aperture to enter and leave the rhomb in a straight line. The gemstone under inspection is positioned so that white light passing through the stone enters

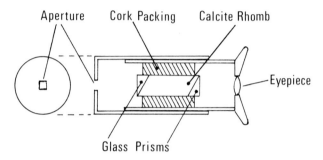

Aperture   Cork Packing   Calcite Rhomb

Eyepiece

Glass Prisms

Fig. 7.1. Diagram showing construction of the prism-type dichroscope

the dichroscope aperture. The two polarised components in the light are then separated by the strong double refraction of the calcite rhomb, and presented to the eyepiece as side-by-side images of the aperture.

If the gemstone is pleochroic, *and is viewed in a direction other than that of an optical axis*, the two images which appear in the eyepiece will differ in shade or colour. If the images are exactly the same colour and shade, then the stone has no pleochroism, and may possibly be singly-refractive.

When testing a stone for pleochroism in this manner, it is important that the gem is viewed in all directions (in the same way as when checking for double refraction on a polariscope), as there will be no visible pleochroic effect if the direction of viewing coincides with an optical axis, or if the directions of polarisation of the gemstone rays and the calcite rhomb are at 45° to each other. To facilitate the inspection of the gemstone, the Rayner dichroscope (*Figure 7.2*) can be fitted with a stone holder attachment, which enables the stone to be rotated until the maximum contrast in shade or colour difference is obtained. As this attachment only provides rotation in one plane, the gemstone should be inspected in at least two different orientations.

Fig. 7.2. The top two dichroscopes by Hanneman and by Hans-Günter Schneider both use polarising filters. The Rayner dichroscope uses a rhomb of Iceland spar

Dichroism in a gemstone can also be detected by using a polarising filter. If the gem is rotated behind such a filter, first one and then the other polarised ray will become visible, and if there is any pleochroism present this will enable consecutive viewing of the shades or colours. Some dichroscopes in fact use polarising filters instead of a rhomb of calcite (*Figure 7.2*), and to obtain simultaneous comparison of pleochroic colours, the filter is cut in half and the two pieces rotated into the 'crossed' position. These are then mounted side-by-side in the end of the viewing tube.

Dispersion

In Chapter 2 we discussed the various ways in which the effect of colour is produced in a gemstone, and these included the selective absorption of light by the gemstone, and the phenomenon of iridescence brought about by structures beneath its surface. Yet another way in which a gemstone can produce colour from white light is by means of its *dispersion*.

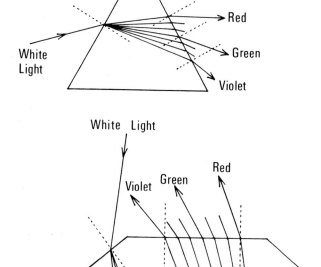

Fig. 7.3. Top: white light entering a glass prism is dispersed into its spectral colours. Bottom: showing dispersion and total internal reflection of white light entering a gemstone

Dispersion is a property (possessed by all gemstones in varying degrees) which causes the individual colour components in white light to be refracted by different amounts as they enter and leave the stone. In a highly dispersive stone, this results in the production of the flashes of coloured light known as 'fire'. The mechanism of dispersion can be seen more clearly with a glass prism, which can be used to split white light up into its spectral colours (*Figure 7.3*). The red component in the light is refracted by the smallest amount and the violet component by the greatest amount.

Although the prismatic colours produced in this way are seen most strikingly in highly dispersive colourless gems (i.e. diamond, zircon, and the synthetic simulants of diamond — rutile, strontium titanate, GGG and cubic zirconium oxide), they are also clearly visible in demantoid garnet and sphene.

The dispersion of a gemstone is a measurable constant, and is defined as the difference between the gem's refractive indices when measured at the B and G Fraunhofer wavelengths. These two wavelengths are standards which can be seen as sharp absorption lines in the sun's spectrum. The B line is in the red at 687 nm, and the G line is in the violet at 430.8 nm. The dispersion of the gemstone is usually measured with the aid of a table spectrometer or goniometer (see Chapter 6) and a special light source which can be set to produce monochromatic light at the B and G wavelengths.

Dispersion can also be measured by means of a calibrated microscope (using the 'direct' RI method). A strong source of white light is needed when using this method, and the refractive indices of the gemstone are measured at the B and G wavelengths by inserting the appropriate interference filters either in the light path, or at the eyepiece of the instrument. Dispersion values for the majority of gemstones are given in the tables in Appendix B.

Reflectivity

The *lustre* of a gemstone can be defined as being the characteristic quality of surface polish obtainable with that stone. As lustre depends on the degree to which light is reflected from the gemstone's surface, it can also be directly related to the stone's *reflectivity*.

The reflectivity of a surface can be measured in absolute terms as the ratio between the intensity of the reflected ray and that of the incident ray:

$$\text{Reflectivity} = \frac{\text{Intensity of reflected ray}}{\text{Intensity of incident ray}}$$

The lustre or reflectivity of a stone, which can be described qualitatively as adamantine, vitreous, resinous, etc., is dependent on several factors, which include the underlying crystalline structure of the mineral, its hardness and its *refractive index*.

The relationship between the gemstone's reflectivity and its refractive index (assuming a 'perfect' surface polish) is, however, probably not a linear one, but is modified by other factors such as molecular structure and transparency. Fresnel's simplified equation, which relates reflectivity to refractive index was formulated for a transparent isotropic mineral in air, and relates to the ideal case where both the incident and reflected rays are normal (i.e. perpendicular) to the surface:

$$\text{Reflectivity} = \frac{(n - A)^2}{(n + A)^2}$$

where n is the refractive index of the gemstone and A is the refractive index of air (= 1.0).

If this simple equation is multiplied by 100, the result becomes the percentage of incident light which is reflected back from the gemstone. Substituting $n = 2.42$ for diamond (and $A = 1.0$ for air) produces a reflectivity figure of 17%. Substituting $n = 1.54$ for quartz produces a reflectivity figure of 4.5%.

It is interesting to note that if the value for A in the equation is increased, the reflectivity of the gemstone decreases. This is the reason why gemstones are often immersed in a liquid having a high RI when inspecting them under a microscope. The

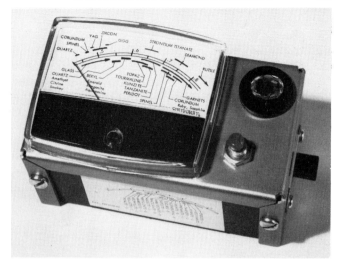

Fig. 7.4. The 'Jeweler's Eye' twin-range reflectivity meter (Hanneman Lapidary Specialties)

immersion technique reduces the amount of light being reflected back from the facets, and thus improves the view of the stone's interior.

In recent years, a variety of electronic reflectivity meters have appeared on the market (*Figure 7.4*). Although most of these are calibrated directly in gemstone names, one model (described as an electronic refractometer) has its scale calibrated directly in RI values. The implication that reflectivity meters could provide the same precision and constancy of measurement as the critical angle refractometer was probably the main reason why the performance of these instruments caused some initial disappointment.

Reflectivity meters are designed to indicate *differences* in reflectivity (i.e. lustre) between the polished surfaces of gemstones, and for this reason they are more accurately described as *relative reflectivity meters*. All instruments of this type use miniature infrared solid-state lamps, known as LEDs (light

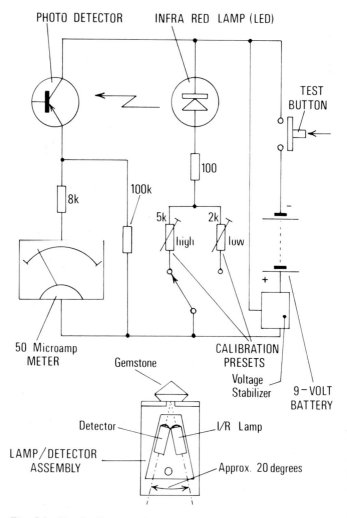

PHOTO DETECTOR   INFRA RED LAMP (LED)

TEST BUTTON

100

8k

100k

5k high   2k low

50 Microamp METER

CALIBRATION PRESETS

Voltage Stabilizer

9 – VOLT BATTERY

Gemstone

Detector   I/R Lamp

LAMP/DETECTOR ASSEMBLY

Approx. 20 degrees

Fig. 7.5. Circuit diagram of a typical two-range reflectivity meter (similar to that used in the Hanneman 'Jeweler's Eye')

emitting diodes), as a convenient and compact source of incident light. A photodiode is mounted alongside the LED, and this is used to detect the amount of infrared energy reflected back from the flat surface of the gemstone under test, and to display this on a suitably calibrated meter (*Figure 7.5*). The intensity of the incident beam is assumed to be constant, and the intensity of the reflected beam, although not an *absolute* measurement of reflectivity, is used to indicate the *relative reflectivity* of the gem. (The instrument is calibrated by means of internal pre-set adjustments, using spinel and a diamond as the test specimens.)

Because it is impractical to set the incident beam perpendicular to the gemstone's surface, and at the same time measure the reflected beam at normal incidence, the angles of incidence and reflection in the reflectivity meter are offset from the normal. For this reason, and because of factors such as birefringence, absorption and surface finish (none of which are allowed for in the reflectivity equation), the relationship between relative reflectivity and refractive index can only be an approximation.

In addition, the use of infrared at 930 nm for the incident beam can result in misleading RI readings on the meter. This is because RI values for gemstones are quoted in terms of yellow monochromatic light at 589.3 nm, and the RI of a gemstone having high dispersion, for instance, would read much lower at 930 nm than at 589.3 nm. The effect of this 'dispersion error' can be seen in the gap that exists between strontium titanate and diamond on the scales of reflectivity meters. Although both stones have almost identical RI values, the dispersion of strontium titanate is more than four times that of diamond. For this reason it is advisable to disregard the theoretical relationship between reflectivity and refractive index, and to use the relative reflectivity meter as a comparative measurement of a stone's *lustre*.

Because this type of instrument is, in effect, measuring the lustre of a gemstone, anything which reduces that lustre, such as dirt, grease or surface scratches, will produce a misleadingly low reading. It is therefore important to check that the surface of the gemstone is in good condition and is thoroughly clean before making a test. (It is also important to keep the test aperture free from dust.) To prevent extraneous light from entering the gemstone under test and increasing the intensity of the light reaching the photodiode, most reflectivity meters are provided with an opaque cap which should be placed over the stone when making a test. Occasionally, the cut of the stone may result in a high reading due to stray internal reflections from the pavilion facets. To avoid being misled by spurious readings of this type, several readings should be taken over the area of the table facet (which must necessarily be large enough to completely cover the test aperture) and any unusually high or low readings disregarded.

Reflectivity meters are particularly useful for checking gem-stones whose refractive indices are too high to be measured on the standard critical angle refractometer. In this context, they enable diamond to be separated quite easily from its many natural and synthetic simulants. However, the critical angle refractometer still excells over the reflectivity meter in the accuracy of its readings, and in the extra information which can be extracted from them (i.e. double refraction, optical character, optic sign).

Critical angle

In Chapter 6, reference was made to the way in which light rays, passing through an optically dense medium, are reflected back from the surface of a less dense medium provided that the angle between the incident rays and normal is greater than the *critical angle* of the two media.

If the denser medium is a gemstone, and the less dense medium is air, as in *Figure 7.6*, the ray I_1 will be reflected back as R_1. At the critical angle of total reflection, however, ray I_2 will cease to obey the law of reflection, and will be refracted along the surface of the gemstone (R_2). At angles less than the critical angle, rays I_3, R_3 will be refracted out of the gemstone into the surrounding air.

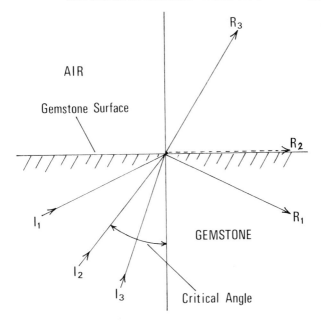

Fig. 7.6. Light rays are reflected back from a gemstone facet at angles to the normal which are greater than the critical angle, and are refracted out of the gemstone at angles less than the critical angle

If a transparent faceted gemstone is to have a bright and sparkling appearance, it is important that as many of the rays as possible entering the gem through its crown facets are reflected back from the pavilion facets, and re-emerge from the stone as a result of *total internal reflection.*

To achieve this condition, the lapidary or diamond polisher must adjust the angles of the crown and pavilion facets so that the majority of rays entering the crown facets meet the interior faces of the pavilion facets at angles to the normal which are *greater* than the critical angle of the stone. If the angles are wrong, the rays will pass out through the pavilion facets, and the stone will appear dark. It is also important that the rays reflected back from the pavilion facets meet the crown facets at angles *less* than the critical angle. If they fail to do this, they will be reflected back into the stone again.

The critical angle of reflection of a gemstone is dependent on both the RI of the gemstone and that of the surrounding medium, as shown in the following equation:

$$\text{Sine of critical angle} = \frac{\text{RI of surrounding medium}}{\text{RI of gemstone}}$$

If the surrounding medium is air,

$$\text{Sine of critical angle} = \frac{1}{\text{RI of gemstone}}$$

$$\text{Critical angle} = \text{Arc sine} \frac{1}{\text{RI of gemstone}}$$

i.e. the angle whose sine is equal to

$$\frac{1}{\text{RI of gemstone}}$$

To determine the critical angle of a gem material in air, its RI value is simply inverted (i.e. divided into 1.0), and this value is taken as the sine of the critical angle. The angle itself can then be derived from a set of trigonometric tables.

For diamond, with an RI of 2.417,

$$\text{Sine of critical angle} = \frac{1}{2.417} = 0.413$$

$$\begin{aligned} \text{Critical angle} &= \text{Arc sine } 0.413 \\ &= 24° \, 26' \end{aligned}$$

For quartz, with an RI of 1.54,

$$\text{Sine of critical angle} = \frac{1}{1.54} = 0.649$$

$$\begin{aligned}\text{Critical angle} &= \text{Arc sine } 0.649 \\ &= 40° \, 30'\end{aligned}$$

From this it can be seen that for optimum brilliance (brought about by total internal reflection), the pavilion/girdle angle for a quartz gemstone will be significantly different from that for a brilliant-cut diamond. In *Figure 7.7* (top diagram), a single ray is shown undergoing total internal reflection in a diamond having a critical angle of $24° \, 26'$. If a quartz gem is cut to the same pavilion/girdle angle as the diamond, this ray would not be reflected back from the pavilion facets as it would meet them at an angle of less than $40° \, 30'$ (the critical angle for quartz). However, if the pavilion/girdle angle is increased from $40°$ to $45°$ (see lower diagram in *Figure 7.7*), the ray would be reflected back successfully through the table facet.

The diagrams in *Figure 7.7* are, of course, very simple ones, and only show the path for those rays which enter the table facet at normal incidence. Ray diagrams which take into account all of the rays entering the crown facet are much more complicated. Because of their complexity they are sometimes plotted with the aid of a computer, which can indicate very quickly the way in which a gemstone's brilliance is affected by varying the stone's facet angles.

The importance of a gemstone's critical angle to its brilliance also has a more down-to-earth aspect. If the pavilion facets of a gemstone are allowed to become contaminated with grease and soap, the result will be a reduction in the stone's overall brilliance. This is because the RI of grease and soap is greater than that for air, and this will *increase* the gem's critical angle (see equation). The effect is particularly noticeable in the case of a brilliant-cut diamond, and is sufficient justification for cleaning the gem regularly in a grease solvent.

116

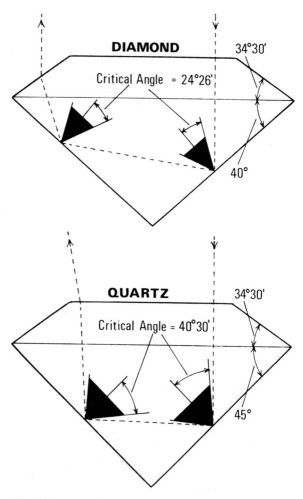

Fig. 7.7. The top diagram shows the total internal reflection of rays meeting the pavilion facets of a diamond at angles greater than the critical angle. In the lower diagram, the pavilion has been made deeper to achieve total internal reflection in quartz which has a larger critical angle

Gemstone cuts

In a colourless transparent gem material, the main requirement is to produce a polished stone which has the maximum brilliance of appearance. This brilliance is determined by two factors, one of which is the degree of reflectivity or lustre which can be achieved by the surface polish, and the other is the ability of the stone to produce total internal reflection of the light rays entering it (*Figure 7.3*). If the gem material has an appreciable degree of dispersion, the cut of the stone must also exploit this to bring out its 'fire'.

The dispersion of white light into its spectral colours to produce the effect of fire reduces the amount of undispersed white light being reflected back from the pavilion facets, and in this case the design of the stone has to strike a balance between fire and brilliance. As incident rays which enter and leave the table facet of the stone at right-angles (i.e. normal) to its surface are not refracted, and are therefore unaffected by the dispersive qualities of the stone, the larger the table area is, the more brilliant will be the appearance of the stone. To achieve more fire, the table area is reduced so that more rays undergo dispersion as they enter or leave the side facets.

In the case of high-value gems such as diamond, the style of the cut may also be influenced by the shape of the rough stone, in order to achieve the best possible 'yield'. For instance, an elongated octahedral crystal may be fashioned into a gemstone having an oblong, oval or pear-shaped profile rather than the traditional round 'brilliant' (see *Figures 7.8, 7.9*) as this will result in a heavier and therefore more valuable end product.

One of the earliest polishing styles for diamond was the *rose cut* (*Figure 7.10*). This had a flat base and a faceted domed top, and although lacking in fire had a reasonable degree of brilliance. The subsequent *brilliant-cut* styles evolved slowly over several hundred years as polishers began to understand the optics associated with diamond's high refractive index, and started adjusting the angles and proportions of the stone's facets to achieve the maximum brilliance and fire.

The modern *brilliant cut* (*Figure 7.11*) consists of fifty-seven facets of which thirty-three are above the girdle forming the crown, and twenty-four are below, forming the pavilion. One extra tiny facet, called the *culet*, is polished on the base of the pavilion as a safety precaution to prevent damage to the exposed point.

The *zircon cut* is similar to the brilliant cut, but because the RI of zircon is lower than that of diamond, an extra eight facets are usually added round the culet to reduce light leakage through the pavilion.

With coloured stones there will also be a need to achieve maximum brilliance through total internal reflection of the

Fig. 7.8. Illustrating various cuts of diamond. The top left is an emerald cut, and the top right is a brilliant cut. The remaining cuts are all based on the brilliant cut (bottom left; marquise; centre; oval; bottom right; pendeloque or pear shape) (De Beers.)

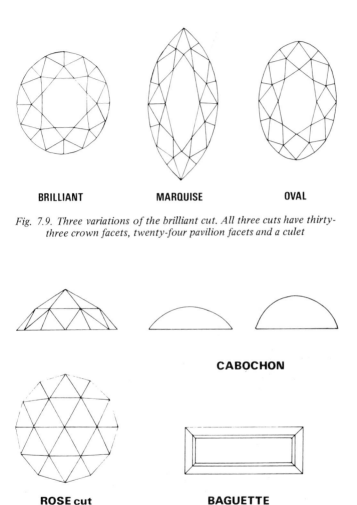

BRILLIANT   **MARQUISE**   **OVAL**

Fig. 7.9. Three variations of the brilliant cut. All three cuts have thirty-three crown facets, twenty-four pavilion facets and a culet

CABOCHON

ROSE cut   **BAGUETTE**

Fig. 7.10. Gemstone cuts showing the early rose cut and the simple domed cabochon form (which is used for opaque, cat's eye and star stones). The baguette is often used for small diamonds

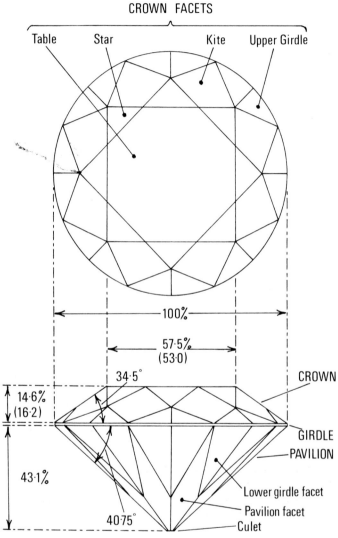

Fig. 7.11. Ideal Scan. DN proportions for the diamond brilliant cut (Tolkowsky proportions are shown in brackets where these differ)

incident light rays, but the cut will also be designed to bring out the gem's body colour to best advantage. The *emerald cut* (which is also known as the *step* or *trap cut*) and the *scissors cut* (*Figure 7.12*) are examples of cutting styles for coloured stones, although they are also used on occasions for colourless gems. The *mixed cut* is also used for coloured gemstones and in particular for sapphires. It consists of a brilliant-cut crown and a step-cut pavilion.

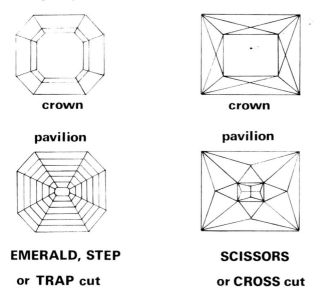

crown   **crown**

pavilion   **pavilion**

EMERALD, STEP   **SCISSORS**

or TRAP cut   **or CROSS cut**

Fig. 7.12. The more traditional cuts which are used principally for coloured gemstones

In some stones, such as blue sapphire, the colour is often unevenly distributed, and the symmetry of the cut is then modified to place the main area of colour low in the pavilion so that it appears to fill the stone when viewed through the crown. With stones having strong pleochroism, the crown will be carefully sited in relation to the stone's optical axis so as to show only the best colour through the table facet.

The simplest gemstone cut is the domed cabochon form, and this is usually reserved for translucent or opaque stones, or those having special optical properties such as chatoyancy or asterism (e.g. tiger's eye or star sapphires and rubies). If the stone is translucent, but the colour is dark, the cabochon will be cut in a shallow profile to lighten the colour. Sometimes the back of the cabochon will be hollow cut to produce the same effect.

Gemstone polishing

The basic method in the polishing of a gemstone (other than diamond) is a combination of rough grinding by the *cutter* to produce the basic facet profile, followed by a finishing operation by the *polisher* to achieve the final facet lustre.

In practice, the rough gemstone material is first sawn into a suitable shape for the cutter by means of a rotating disc charged with diamond or carborundum particles, the material usually being hand-held against the cutting edge of the disc.

The sawn 'blank' is then passed to the cutter who grinds the facets on the stone, using diamond dust, carborundum powder or an emery abrasive on a rotating horizontal cast iron or copper lap. The facet angles are controlled either entirely by eye, with an occasional check under a hand lens, or by using one of the modern semi-automatic dops, which enables the stone to be rotated to the precise facet angles. At the end of this operation, all the facets have been ground on the gem, but they have been left with a rough matt finish.

The gemstone is then cleaned thoroughly to remove all traces of the coarse abrasive, and passed to the polisher to produce the final high-gloss lustre on the facet surfaces. This final polishing is performed on a leather or material-covered copper or wooden lap, which is impregnated with a 'softer' abrasive such as cerium oxide, jeweller's rouge (powdered haematite) or green rouge (chromium oxide).

While 'hand cutting' is still used for the more expensive gemstones, many other stones, including the synthetics, are faceted by automatic machines. In the Gilson synthetic works, these machines are programmed to produce the various styles of cut by means of a punched card system.

For both manual and automatic polishing the growing trend these days is to use graded diamond powders or diamond compounds (i.e. diamond powder mixed with Lanolin cream) for both cutting and polishing operations, starting with 60 to 90 micron size for rough stock removal, and progressing through 30 to 60 micron grade for shaping, and 6 to 12 micron grade for the pre-polishing finish, to reach 1 to 6 micron grade for the final polish.

For many years, both cutting and polishing processes were thought to be entirely abrasive, the final surface polish being brought about by finer and finer degrees of grinding. At the beginning of this century, however, G. T. Beilby discovered that, with the exception of diamond, the final high polish on a gemstone is produced not by abrasive action, but by the high lapping temperature which causes the surface layer of the stone to flow in a liquid-like manner. The resulting highly reflective skin is called the *Beilby layer*, and effectively covers over the polishing marks in the surface below.

With gemstones like corundum and quartz, the Beilby layer produced in this way immediately re-crystallises again to conform to the gem's crystal structure. In other stones, such as calcite and kyanite, the Beilby layer tends to solidify as a molecular layer of amorphous material, which only re-crystallises if it is parallel to a principal crystal plane. With stones such as spinel and zircon, the Beilby layer solidifies on all surfaces as an amorphous skin, but because of its extreme thinness, it has no effect on the optical indices of doubly-refracting stones when these are measured on a refractometer.

Because of diamond's high melting point, the polish achieved on its facets is not due to the formation of a Beilby layer but is entirely a product of fine abrasive action. This factor, and its extreme hardness, makes the faceting of diamond significantly different from that of other gemstones in both equipment and technique.

Starting with the rough diamond crystal, an expert inspects the stone and decides how it should be cut to produce the best yield in polished stones. He then marks the surface of the stone with indian ink to indicate the directions in which the stone must be sawn or cleaved (with larger stones, both methods may be employed).

Cleaving is performed by first scratching a shallow groove in the surface of the diamond — see *Figure 4.2*. A thin-bladed chisel is then placed in the groove and given a sharp blow to part the stone along the line of the cleavage plane.

Sawing is carried out using a thin rigidly clamped phosphor bronze blade which is impregnated with fine diamond dust and rotated at 5000 r.p.m.. Sawing can only take place in two directions across the crystal grain, one of these directions being parallel to the natural girdle of the octahedral crystal (*Figure 4.1*) and the other is at right-angles to this through the tips of the bi-pyramids and the centres of their common baselines.

The sawn or cleaved stone is then rounded or *bruted* by rotating it on a spindle, and bringing another diamond into contact with it as a cutting tool.

Next, the crown and pavilion facets are ground by mounting the bruted stone in a holder called a *dop* and bringing it into contact with the surface of a 12-in diameter iron lap called a *scaife* (*Figure 7.13*). This is dressed with a mixture of olive oil and diamond dust and rotated at 3000 r.p.m..

Two types of dop are used, the older version which employs low-melting point solder to secure the diamond, and the modern type dop which uses a mechanical clamping device. Both types of dop are mounted on a copper rod which is bent by hand to the appropriate facet angle. The rod is held in a saddle-shaped *tang,* which is weighted to achieve the correct grinding pressure (*Figure 7.3*). In modern mechanical dops, the angles of the facets are indexed by the dop mechanism. In either case, the polisher grinds the crown and pavilion facets in a fixed sequence, checking the depth of each one by eye before proceeding to the next.

Several fully automatic diamond faceting machines have been developed, and these are mainly designed for the polishing of small diamonds in order to reduce labour costs. One such machine, the Piermatic, was originated by a subsidiary company

Fig. 7.13. A group of three diamonds being polished in mechanical dops. The dops are mounted in tangs which are weighted to produce the correct pressure between the diamond and the rotating scaife (De Beers.)

of De Beers, and is now in use in all major cutting centres.

The work of faceting the diamond is usually divided up between three experts. The *bruter*, as already mentioned, produces the basic rounded profile. *The cross cutter* then takes the stone and grinds the table, the sixteen main crown and pavilion facets, and the culet. If the cross cutter has found it necessary to polish his sequence of facets slightly off the centre line of the stone (in order to remove a surface inclusion or flaw), the stone will then be returned to the bruter to re-grind the girdle so that it is symmetrical with the facets. The stone is finally passed to the *brillianteerer*, who grinds the final sequence of twenty-four crown and sixteen pavilion facets, and gives all the facets their finishing polish.

8 Absorption and Emission Spectra

In the majority of gemstones, colour is due to the presence in the stone of one or more of the eight *transition elements* (see Chapter 2). These elements are either present as impurities (e.g. chromium in ruby, nickel in chrysoprase) or as an integral part of the gem's chemical composition (e.g. copper in malachite, manganese in rhodonite). In either case they produce the effect of colour by absorbing certain wavelengths from the white light as it passes through the stone, or as it is reflected from its surface. This phenomenon is called *selective absorption*, and can be made visible by means of an instrument called a spectroscope, which uses prisms to spread out the light from the gemstone into its spectral colours. The result is called an absorption spectrum, in which the colours or wavelengths absorbed by the gemstone appear as dark bands.

It was Sir Isaac Newton in 1666 who first demonstrated that white light was composed of a continuous spectrum of colours ranging from red at one end to violet at the other. His equipment, which consisted of a circular aperture to admit a beam of daylight into a darkened room and a glass prism to disperse this light into its component colours, resulted in the overlapping of adjacent colours, and produced only a poorly defined spectrum. It was not until 1814 that a Bavarian optician and scientist by the name of Fraunhofer, using a finer aperture to admit the light, together with a viewing telescope, refined this experiment and showed that the white light radiated from the sun contained an absorption spectrum composed of a series of fine lines.

These were subsequently called *Fraunhofer lines*, and were later found by the German scientists Kirchhoff and Bunsen to be due mainly to the absorption of certain characteristic wave-lengths by the vapour of various elements in the chromosphere surrounding the sun. The first recorded use of the spectroscope to observe absorption spectra in gemstones came in 1866 when Sir Arthur Church wrote a letter to the *Intellectual Observer* describing his discovery of absorption bands in specimens of Ceylon zircons and almandine garnets.

The prism spectroscope

The early spectroscopes devised by Zantedeschi, Kirchhoff and Bunsen comprised a small aperture or slit to admit the light, a converging lens, a prism and a viewing telescope. The most important refinement was in the collimation of the in-cident light. This was brought about by placing the aperture in the focal plane of the converging lens, thus ensuring that only parallel rays entered the prism. The result was the pro-duction of a 'pure' spectrum (i.e. one in which there was no overlap, or contamination, between the component colours).

The main limitation of the early single-prism spectroscope was that the angle of dispersion was too small to allow for de-tailed examination of the spectrum. One way of increasing the angle of dispersion was to use several prisms. However, the deviation angle between the incoming incident light and the emergent spectrum (see *Figure 7.3* in Chapter 7) became greater as each prism was added, and set a practical limitation to this method of increasing the instrument's dispersion.

To achieve a reasonably compact 'in line' instrument with a usable angle of dispersion, it became necessary to design a multiple prism which had zero deviation between the incident light and the centre line of the emerging spectrum. In 1860, Amici produced a compound prism which used crown and flint glass components of differing refractive indices to give dispersion without deviation (*Figure 8.1*).

The construction of a modern 'direct vision' spectroscope using a triple-element Amici prism can be seen in *Figure 8.2*. One of the important components of the spectroscope is the

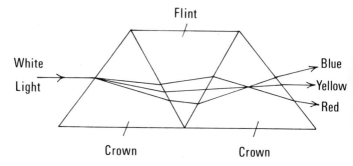

Fig. 8.1. Showing the three components of an Amici compound prism whose differing refractive indices are chosen to give zero deviation of the yellow ray in the emerging spectrum

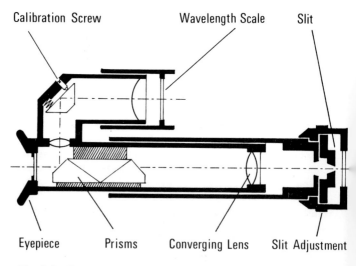

Fig. 8.2. Construction of a direct vision prism spectroscope with built-in wavelength scale

aperture or slit through which the light to be analysed passes. The spectrum produced by the optics of the instrument is in fact a series of images of this slit. If the slit is wide, these images will overlap (as they did in Newton's experiment) and the resulting spectrum will not be pure. For this reason, most spectroscopes are made with an adjustable slit which can be set for a resolution which is relevant to the spectrum being analysed. The setting of the slit width is usually a compromise between obtaining the maximum definition for fine lines, and letting enough light in to produce a visible spectrum. When initially setting the slit and focusing the eyepiece, the spectroscope can be pointed at daylight and the adjustments made for best resolution of the Fraunhofer lines. Alternatively, the spectral lines in the light from a sodium or a fluorescent lamp can be used.

As mentioned earlier, another condition for the production of a pure spectrum is that the light rays falling on the first prism

(a)

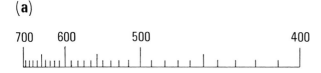

Wavelengths in nanometres – multiply by ten for Ångström units, divide by one thousand for micrometres
⟨μm⟩

(b)

Fig. 8.3. The wavelength scale of the prism spectroscope is cramped at the red end, and spread out at the violet end (a). The linear scale of the diffraction grating spectroscope is shown at (b)

in the series are parallel. This condition is met by inserting a converging lens between the slit and the prism, and positioning this lens so that its focal plane is coincident with the slit.

An added refinement to the spectroscope is the provision of a calibrated wavelength scale, which, by means of a separate light source and suitable ancillary optics, is superimposed on the image of the spectrum. A calibrating screw is generally provided which enables the scale to be moved relative to the spectrum. This adjustment is usually made when viewing a sodium source, so that the 589.3 nm point on the scale can be set to coincide with the sodium emission line. In some instruments a calibrated knob moves the spectrum relative to a fixed cursor, the wavelength reading being computed from the control knob reading.

The wavelengths in the spectrum produced by a prism-type instrument are not linearly spaced out, but, due to dispersion, are bunched at the red end and spread out at the blue/violet end (*Figure 8.3(a)*). This makes it more difficult to resolve closely spaced lines at the red end of the spectrum, and, if the measurement of wavelength is important, makes the provision of a superimposed wavelength scale essential.

The diffraction grating spectroscope

This instrument uses a diffraction grating to disperse the light into its spectral components. The grating usually takes the form of a plate of glass on which are printed a series of faint parallel lines. The pitch of the lines is in the order of 15 000 to 30 000 per inch, and these are printed on the glass photographically by optical reduction from a much larger master negative.

Although the diffraction grating spectroscope may appear to be a simpler instrument than its prism counterpart, its principle of operation is quite complex and involves both diffraction and interference phenomena. The construction of a typical diffraction spectroscope is similar in some respects to that of the prism version. The slit lies in the focal plane of

a converging lens and acts with it as a collimator, causing the
incident light to fall as parallel rays normal to the plane of
the grating. The grating produces a series of diffracted beams,
the main one being focused and displayed by means of the
eyepiece.

The resulting spectrum is not so pure or bright as that
obtained with a prism spectroscope, as multiple spectra are
also produced on each side of the main one and tend to dilute
it. For this reason it is better for the student to use a prism
spectroscope until he has become familiar with the techniques
of observing absorption spectra. The diffraction grating spectroscope does, however, have one advantage over the prism type
in that the wavelengths are evenly spaced out across the width
of the spectrum (*Figure 8.3(b)*).

The non-destructive testing of a gemstone by means of its
absorption spectrum represents a small part of the total science
of spectroscopy. In industry, spectroscopy is used in the
measurement of the constituent elements in a sample by
vaporising it in an electric arc (or in a laser beam) and
inspecting a photographic record of the resulting spectrum.
Spectroscopy is also used to inspect the infrared (IR) and
ultraviolet (UV) regions of the non-visible spectrum, and
absorption bands here are displayed graphically by means
of recording spectrometers which plot the IR and UV responses
on built-in chart recorders.

Use of spectra for gemstone identification

While the spectroscope may require more expertise in its use
than the refractometer, it comes into its own when identifying
either faceted gemstones whose refractive indices are too high
to be measured on the refractometer, or unpolished gem
mineral samples. There are also some occasions when the
spectroscope may be the only means of distinguishing a
naturally coloured gem from a treated one.

For gemmological work we are primarily interested in using
the spectroscope to inspect the way in which the gemstone
under test has modified the spectrum of white light passing

through the stone or reflected from its surface. As most of the transition elements can be associated with characteristic groups of absorption bands or lines, it is possible with some coloured gemstones to identify the stone positively by means of its absorption spectrum alone.

There are also stones such as zircon, apatite and YAG which may show a 'fine line' spectrum due to the presence of either radioactive or 'rare earth' elements. These lines are often so evenly distributed along the spectrum that they have little overall effect on the stone's colour.

Figure 8.4 shows a few of the more important gemstone spectra. For a more complete range, reference should be made to Anderson's *Gem Testing,* or Liddicoat's *Handbook of Gem Identification* (see bibliography in Appendix C). To avoid any confusion when referring to gemmological textbooks (particularly American ones) it should be remembered that the convention for viewing and illustrating spectra in the UK is to place *red* on the left, while in the USA the convention is to place *violet* on the left.

So far we have considered only the presence of absorption lines or bands in the light spectrum. In some cases it is possible for the energy in the light source, which is illuminating the gemstone under inspection, to stimulate the colouring elements in the stone so that instead of absorbing characteristic wavelengths in the incident light, they emit light at these same wavelengths to produce *fluorescent* lines.

The most important of the gemstones which show fluorescent emission lines in their spectra are ruby and red spinel. With both of these stones, the emission lines appear at the red end of the spectrum and are due to the presence of chromium. In order to see the lines more clearly with the spectroscope it is advisable to place a blue filter in front of the light source so that the red/orange end of the spectrum is effectively blocked out. This technique can also be used to advantage when inspecting absorption lines or bands in the blue end of a stone's spectrum.

The ruby spectrum at the top of *Figure 8.4* is one of the most distinctive of all the gemstone spectra, and enables this

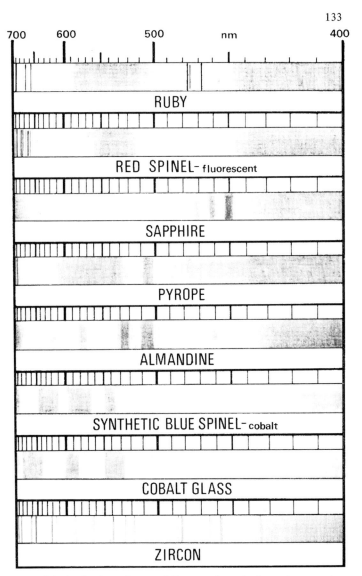

Fig. 8.4. A selection of some of the more important gemstone spectra

gem to be positively identified and separated from other stones of similar appearance (i.e. red spinel, pyrope and almandine garnet, red zircon). The absorption lines and bands in the ruby spectrum are caused by chromium. The line in the deep red at 690 nm is, in fact, a pair of closely spaced lines (known as a *doublet*). This is usually seen as a single bright fluorescing line when the stone is viewed in reflected light, or as a single absorption line when using transmitted light. There are also two weak lines centred on 660 nm, and a wide absorption band in the yellow/green part of the spectrum. The doublet in the deep red, together with the narrow bands in the blue, make this spectrum diagnostic for ruby. Some natural rubies contain iron, and this has an inhibiting influence on the deep red fluorescing doublet. Rubies from Thailand, for instance, often contain sufficient iron to completely suppress the doublet. The iron in these rubies is also the reason for their dark almandine colour.

The absorption spectra of synthetic ruby is, unfortunately, identical to that obtained with the natural stone, except that the lines and bands tend to be more intense, and this makes them easier to observe (methods of distinguishing between natural and synthetic gems are described in Chapter 11).

Red spinel, like ruby, is also coloured by chromium, and shows the characteristic emission lines in the deep red. These are usually more numerous than in ruby, and in the bright red chrome-rich types the lines are prominent enough to be described as 'organ pipes'. Unlike ruby, there are no bands in the blue.

The presence of iron in natural blue, green and yellow sapphires is indicated by three broad absorption bands in the blue, although occasionally only the band at 450 nm is visible. In synthetic green and yellow sapphires, which are coloured with nickel, these bands are absent. In synthetic blue sapphires, which are coloured with iron and titanium, most of the iron evaporates out of the boule during the crystal growing process and is therefore not present in sufficient quantity to produce these three typical absorption bands. Very occasionally, however, a faint band can be detected in the region of 450 nm with synthetic blue sapphires. Australian and Thailand sapphires normally contain sufficient iron to produce all three bands in reasonable strength, and with blue sapphires this results in darker shades, often with a hint of green. In contrast, Sri Lankan sapphires are deficient in iron, and only a very weak 450 nm band is normally visible in these stones.

While both pyrope and almandine contain iron, which in almandine is indicated by three bands in the yellow, green and green/blue, all but the green/blue iron band is obscured in pyrope by the presence of chromium, which produces a wide absorption band in the yellow/green. The fact that the almandine absorption bands appear very different from the iron spectra seen in sapphire is due to the way in which the colouring impurity affects the light when contained in different mineral structures.

Synthetic blue spinel is coloured by cobalt. The three broad characteristic cobalt bands in the orange, yellow and green sections of the spectrum serve to distinguish synthetic from natural blue spinel, which shows a broad complex structure due to iron. The blue gemstone simulant, cobalt glass, also shows a distinctive cobalt spectrum, but in this case the centre band is narrower, and is shifted towards the orange section of the spectrum, while the two outer bands are spaced further apart.

The spectrum obtained with zircon can be rather variable, ranging from a fine line spectrum (due to uranium) in yellow and green stones, to no lines at all in some red zircons. In those zircons (other than the red exceptions) which do not exhibit a fine line spectrum, there is usually a line visible at 653.5 nm.

Chrysoprase is a relatively rare and expensive green crypto-crystalline quartz, and can be difficult to distinguish from other less costly green chalcedonies such as chrome-coloured and green-stained varieties. However, unlike chrysoprase, none of the other varieties owe their colour to nickel, and the only way to distinguish the genuine gemstone is to use a spectro-scope to look for the narrow nickel absorption band at 632 nm.

Chrome chalcedony can, in turn, be distinguished from green-stained specimens by its strong chromium doublet in the deep red.

With diamonds the absorption bands tend to be weak and difficult to detect. In yellow Cape diamonds there is a band in the violet at 415.5 nm, with associated weaker bands at 435, 451 and 478 nm; the deeper the yellow shade is, the more prominent are the bands. In brown diamonds the principal band is at 504 nm, with a weaker one at 498 nm.

The spectroscope has featured prominently in the detection of poorly coloured yellow Cape diamonds whose colour has been artificially improved by neutron irradiation followed by heat treatment at 800 °C. The detection of stones treated in this way has become important because of the high rarity price fetched by 'fancy' coloured diamonds, and the possibility of the fraudulent sale of treated stones as 'fancies'. With the irradiated and heat-treated diamonds there is a tell-tale narrow absorption band in the deep yellow at 594 nm, which is not present in naturally coloured stones, and for several years this has served as the main diagnostic indicator.

In 1978, however, researchers at Kings College, London, discovered that if an irradiated diamond is heated to 1000 °C, the 594 nm diagnostic band disappears completely and permanently. The absence of the 594 nm band can therefore no longer be taken as a positive indication that a diamond is naturally coloured. Tests for artificially coloured diamonds are now based on even fainter bands at 504nm and 498nm (induced by the new colour), and these can only be reliably detected after cooling the diamond in liquid nitrogen. If these are present, in association with the original yellow Cape band at 415.5 nm, this is proof that the diamond has been artificially coloured.

Apart from its use in identifying gemstones by means of their absorption spectra, the spectroscope can also be employed to distinguish between naturally coloured and dyed gem materials. Poorly coloured jadeite is sometimes stained to imitate the more expensive green variety. Naturally coloured green jadeite owes its colour to chromium, and a vague doublet can usually be detected at 691.5 nm, with a pair of weaker lines at 655.0 nm and 630.0 nm. An intense iron band can also be seen in reflected light at 437.0 nm. If the green colour of the jadeite is due to staining, none of these bands will be visible, but the dye will produce a broad absorption band in the red.

Fine line spectra and the rare earths

The fine line spectra seen in some zircons have some similarity to those produced by apatite, synthetic scheelite, the synthetic garnets and by some types of glass. However, the spectral lines developed by these latter materials are generally much more prominent than those in the zircon spectrum, and are due to the presence of 'rare earth' elements such as erbium and didymium. Although these rare earth spectra are useful as identifying features, in general they play no part in the production of colour. They can sometimes be seen in the synthetic diamond simulants (i.e YAG, GGG, scheelite) which are often doped with one of the rare earth elements.

Using the spectroscope

Before putting the spectroscope into use, the slit adjustment should be set to a partially open position, and the instrument focused on either the Fraunhofer lines (by pointing it at daylight) or on the lines in a sodium or fluorescent light source. The next move is to illuminate the specimen so that sufficient light can pass through it (or be reflected from it) to form a visible spectrum.

One of the most important pieces of ancillary equipment for use with the spectroscope is, in fact, a source of strong white light. In some composite spectroscope units, this is built in, together with a cooling fan and a heat filter, which prevent the specimen from being over-heated. There are several commercial light sources available which use flexible

Fig. 8.5. The author using an Eickhorst coldlight spectroscope

glass-fibre light guides to inject the light into the specimen at
the most advantageous angle (*Figure 8.5*).

Even when the infrared end of the emission from a light
source is removed by means of a heat filter, there is still a con-
siderable amount of energy contained in the light, and it is
not advisable to leave a stone exposed to a strong source for
too long. Over-exposure can, for example, affect the colour of
a zircon, and if a stone contains a stress defect or crack, the
light energy may cause this to extend into a fracture.

If a microscope is to hand, it is also possible to use this as
a convenient mounting for the spectroscope and as a means of
illuminating the gemstone under test. The specimen is placed
on the microscope stage, the microscope set for its lowest
magnification factor, and the eyepiece removed. The source of
illumination, the position of the gemstone, and the focus of
the microscope are adjusted so that the microscope viewing
tube is filled evenly with the body colour of the gem. To avoid

being temporarily blinded by the strong light emerging from the viewing tube, it is advisable while making this adjustment to place a piece of ground or opal glass on top of the viewing tube.

If the microscope is fitted with a built-in illuminator, this should be set for light-field work when inspecting a transparent gem. If an iris is fitted, this should be adjusted so that the minimum of light escapes round the edges of the specimen. For opaque gems, an incident light source must be used, and this may be employed to advantage on transparent/translucent gems.

Having correctly illuminated the gemstone, the spectroscope can now be lowered into the viewing tube and final adjustments made to the slit and focus controls to achieve the clearest spectrum. It should be noted that the focus settings differ slightly from the red to the violet end of the spectrum, and small adjustments may be necessary when inspecting lines at both ends of the spectrum. With strongly dichroic stones it should also be remembered that there will be a difference between the spectrum produced by the ordinary ray and that produced by the extraordinary ray. For this reason, such a stone should be rotated so that any change in spectra can be noted before making a diagnosis (e.g. with ruby, the central absorption band in the yellow/green is broader and stronger for one ray than for the other). This difference can also be detected by placing a polarising filter over the eyepiece.

With most people, the eye's visual sensitivity becomes weaker towards the violet end of the spectrum. For this reason, difficulty is often experienced in seeing lines or bands at these wavelengths. Some improvement can be gained by illuminating the gemstone under test with a blue rather than a white light, as this will enhance the contrast of any bands at the blue end of the spectrum. It is also helpful to allow the eyes to become dark-adapted before searching for faint lines and bands, and to keep the level of the room illumination as low as possible. It is also inadvisable to stare at a brilliantly lit spectrum for even a short period as this will reduce the sensitivity of the eye. Weak bands can sometimes be detected by looking slightly away from the section of spectrum under investigation and using the more sensitive peripheral area of vision.

9 Luminescent and Electrical Properties of Gems

When some substances acquire surplus energy in one form or another, below the level which would cause incandescence, they respond by emitting a visible 'cold' radiation, which is often characteristic for that substance. The mechanism producing this cold radiation, or *luminescence*, is associated with the excitation of atoms within the substance. The energy absorbed by luminescing materials is expended in moving electrons out of their normal atomic orbits (known as the 'ground' state) into orbits of a higher energy level (known as the 'excited' state). When these electrons eventually return to their more stable orbits, they give up their surplus energy in the form of an electromagnetic radiation (i.e. visible or, occasionally, ultraviolet light).

Of the many varieties of luminescence which can occur, *photoluminescence* is the most interesting and useful for gemmological purposes. With this type of luminescence, the input energy is in the form of electromagnetic radiation (i.e. visible light, ultraviolet light or X-rays), and the output radiation has a longer wavelength than that of the original excitation.

The orbital oscillations of the electrons in a luminescing material occur in a random fashion. If there is virtually no delay between the electrons acquiring energy and then releasing it as visible light, the phenomenon is called *fluorescence*, and ceases immediately the source of excitation is switched off. If, however, there is a discernible delay before the electrons give up their surplus energy, the phenomenon is called *phosphorescence*, and can be seen as an 'afterglow' when the excitation ceases. It is possible for a material to both fluoresce and phosphoresce, and the result is sometimes seen as a change in luminescent colour when the source of irradiation is switched off. Some materials have the ability to store the energy they acquire from electromagnetic radiation and then to release it again when heated, and this effect is called *thermophosphorescence.*

While photoluminescence is produced by electromagnetic radiation in the visible and near visible spectrum, the sources of energy which cause *triboluminescence, cathodoluminescence* and *electroluminescence* are quite different. A triboluminescing material is one which glows when it is rubbed or abraded. In practice, this can occur when a rough diamond is being polished on a scaife, and results in the stone glowing an intense blue or red. If the stone is raised out of contact with the surface of the scaife, the fluorescent effect immediately vanishes, proving that it was generated by friction and not by heat.

Cathodoluminescence is a fluorescent effect displayed by some materials when they are bombarded with a beam of electrons. While the phosphors used on the screen of television tubes are common everyday examples of cathodoluminescing materials, cathodoluminescence in minerals was first discovered as a side effect when viewing samples in an electron microscope. It has since been developed into a useful research tool for detecting the presence of rare earths and specific minerals in agglomerates. It is also used for investigating crystallographic features and nitrogen 'platelets' in diamond crystals.

Yet another form of luminescence can be produced in some substances by passing an electric current through them, and when this occurs the substance is said to be *electroluminescent.* Natural blue diamonds are semiconductors (i.e. like the 'doped' silicon used in microprocessors, their electrical conductivity lies somewhere between that of a conductor and an insulator), and one of the tests used to distinguish them from artificially coloured blue diamonds (which do not conduct electricity) is to apply a direct or alternating voltage to them via a current indicator. During this test, natural blue diamonds often exhibit electroluminescence under the influence of the current flowing through the crystal lattice.

In all these various forms of luminescence, the light emitted is either due to some intrinsic property in the material (e.g. the lattice defects in diamond) or to the presence of luminescent impurities called *activators* (e.g. chromic oxide in ruby).

For the purposes of gemstone identification, the fact that the emitted photoluminescent light is always of a longer wavelength than the applied irradiation is of prime importance. The effect of this wavelength 'conversion' means that it is possible to use short-wave irradiation sources in the form of ultraviolet lamps and X-ray generators to produce visible luminescent effects. With some gemstones, even the short-wavelength visible light at the blue end of the spectrum can be used to produce a longer-wavelength emission at the red end of the spectrum.

This latter phenomenon was first put to practical use in gemmology by B. W. Anderson, who adapted the technique of crossed filters for the identification of gemstones in the Gem Testing Laboratory of the London Chamber of Commerce. It must be pointed out that the crossed filter method has nothing to do with polarising filters, as might first be thought, but involves the use of colour filters.

The various forms of electromagnetic radiation available to the gemmologist are, in fact, visible light, long-wave ultraviolet light, short-wave ultraviolet light and X-rays. Each of these forms of energy has its particular application in the identification of gemstones by means of their luminescent properties. The techniques and equipment associated with each of the four forms of radiation will now be discussed in more detail.

Crossed filters

This is the simplest of all the methods used to test for luminescence in that the necessary equipment is generally to hand, and is not specialised. All that is needed is a strong source of white light, a blue filter and a red filter. These filters can be of the simple gelatine variety sandwiched between sheets of glass to protect them from the heat of the lamp. Alternatively, if a flask of copper sulphate solution is used in place of the blue filter, this will also serve as a combined heat filter and condensing lens.

The blue filter is placed between the light source and the gemstone, and the gemstone is viewed through the red filter. If only the blue filtered light is allowed to fall on the gemstone (by suitable shielding), and the stone is seen to glow when viewed through the red filter, it must be fluorescing.

Gemstones which demonstrate their fluorescence most readily under crossed filters are those which owe their coloration to chromium-rich impurities. Such gemstones are principally ruby and red spinel, both natural and synthetic.

Emerald, pink topaz and the rare alexandrite variety of chrysoberyl also fluoresce red under the crossed filters, although this may be inhibited in emerald and alexandrite by the presence of iron, even in small quantities. For this reason, synthetic emerald fluoresces more strongly than natural stones, as the latter often contain traces of iron. Pyrope and jadeite, which contain both chromium and iron, do not fluoresce at all. Natural black pearls fluoresce with a faint red glow which distinguishes them from those artificially stained with silver nitrate.

Long-wave ultraviolet lamps

Ultraviolet radiation sources are mercury discharge lamps as these have strong spectral emission lines ranging from yellow to the far ultraviolet. The dominant mercury emission line which is used for long-wave (LW) ultraviolet work has a wavelength of 366 nm. To avoid the luminescence of a gemstone being masked by the visible emission lines in the mercury lamp's spectrum, a filter is used which blocks out most of the visible light rays.

The filter used for LW ultraviolet lamps is a Wood's glass filter, which contains cobalt and a trace of nickel. One commerical version of this is the Chance filter OX1, which is available as a 50 × 50 mm glass square from Gemmological Instruments Ltd. The mercury lamp used for LW work is a high-pressure discharge type. LW ultraviolet lamp units are manufactured in a variety of forms.

Short-wave ultraviolet lamps

The mercury lamp used for short-wave (SW) ultraviolet work is a low-pressure vapour type, using a quartz tube or envelope. The SW mercury line at 254 nm is dominant in the emission spectrum of this lamp, and a Chance OX7 filter is used to pass this wavelength while filtering out most of the visible light in the lamp's emission spectrum.

It should be noted that SW ultraviolet filters deteriorate during use and should be checked for efficiency after about 100

Fig. 9.1. This unit contains both long-wave and short-wave lamps in a lightproof viewing cabinet (Gemmological Instruments Ltd.)

hours of operation. LW and SW lamps also suffer a loss of efficiency during use, and their output may fall by up to 20% in the first 100 hours. Some ultraviolet units are fitted with independently controlled LW and SW lamps, which permit rapid comparison of a material's luminescent properties at these two wavelengths (*Figure 9.1*).

X-ray equipment

Because of the size and cost of the equipment, and the pre-cautions necessary to protect users against radiation dangers, X-ray sources are generally only found in the research labora-tory. For diagnostic gemmology, X-rays are used either as a

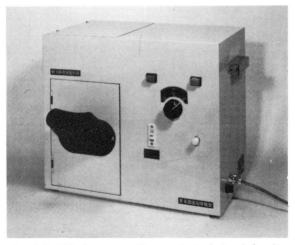

Fig. 9.2. This low-power X-ray unit is designed for dis-tinguishing diamond from its simulants by testing specimens for their transparency to X-rays (GAAJ)

source of energy to stimulate luminescence in gemstones, or as a means of penetrating gem materials to provide information on their internal structures. The wavelengths of X-rays lie between 0.1 and 1.0 nm, and this enables the rays to penetrate with ease those substances whose constituent elements have a low atomic weight. Diamond, for instance, which is composed of carbon, is virtually transparent to X-rays, while all other gem minerals show varying degrees of opacity depending on the atomic weights of the constituent elements.

Diamonds' transparency to X-rays is used as a method of distinguishing between them and their simulants in the X-ray diamond tester shown in *Figure 9.2*. Test specimens are placed on a reflecting fluorescent plate inside the unit, and when the operate button is pressed, the internal X-ray tube is energised and the opacity of the specimen can be seen as a shadow profile through the viewing window.

In crystallographic research, X-rays are used to explore the structure and symmetry of crystal systems. A narrow beam of X-rays is injected into the specimen in the direction of a crystal axis and produces a distinct pattern of spots on a photographic film. This is known as a *transmission Laue pattern* and is the result of the X-rays being diffracted by the regular three-dimensional grating formed by atoms in the crystal's lattice. The technique can also be used to distinguish between natural and cultured pearls (see Chapter 10).

When used in *X-ray topography*, the beam is focused into a narrow ribbon, and scanned slowly across the specimen to produce a photographic record of the crystal's internal defects. This technique has been used experimentally to 'fingerprint' both polished and rough diamonds for documentation purposes, and as a method of distinguishing between natural and synthetic emerald.

Identifying gemstones by luminescence

Although not many gem materials have luminescent properties, when luminescence is present it can sometimes help to identify a gemstone, particularly if the luminescing colour under LW UV is different to that under SW UV. The following notes indicate some of the typical colours which can be seen when certain gemstones are subjected to LW and SW UV light, and to X-ray irradiation.

Apatite

This has the most varied luminescent range of all the gemstones. As its colours vary with both the type of irradiation and the body colour of the gemstone, they are listed here in tabular form for clarity.

Body colour	LW UV	SW UV	X-rays
yellow	lilac	lilac/pink	pinkish-white/yellow
blue	dark blue	to light blue	faint pinkish straw
green	mustard yellow	weak mustard	yellowish-white
violet	greenish yellow	pale mauve	bright greenish-yellow with persistent phosphorescence

Benitoite

This rare gemstone is normally inert under LW UV, but glows bright blue under SW UV. Pale blue to colourless specimens may, however, fluoresce a dull red under LW UV.

Danburite

This can be identified under LW UV by its sky-blue fluorescence.

Diamond

All diamonds fluoresce a chalky blue under X-rays, and this is the basis of the separation technique used in diamond mines. However, only about 10 to 15% of all diamonds fluoresce under UV light. These are mainly Cape series diamonds (i.e. those having a yellow body colour), and under LW UV their fluorescent colours range from blue through green to yellow, with an occasional pink and red.

Those diamonds which fluoresce blue also show a faint yellow phosphorescence. The eyes need to be dark-adapted to detect this persistent yellow afterglow, but when seen it is confirmatory for diamond, as there are no other blue-fluorescing gem minerals which exhibit a yellow phosphorescence. In general, diamonds show less luminescence under SW UV, although blue-fluorescing stones sometimes show the typical yellow afterglow more clearly after SW irradiation.

Because of the very variable fluorescent properties of diamond under LW UV, R. Webster once suggested its use as a method of identifying a piece of diamond-set jewellery, the various strengths and colours of fluorescence acting as 'passport features' when photographed in UV light. By the same token, the technique can also be used to obtain an impression of the genuiness of the diamonds. If all the stones fluoresce with identical colour and strength they are more likely to be simulants, or even paste (particularly if this occurs under SW UV).

Emerald

Although natural emeralds show some response under LW UV, they are best tested for fluorescence using the crossed filter method. Most synthetic emeralds, however, show a distinctive crimson fluorescence under both LW and SW UV.

Fluorspar

With the exception of 'Blue John', which is completely inert, most varieties show some fluorescence under LW UV, which at its best is a bright blue/violet. Some specimens show a phosphorescent effect after exposure to X-rays. After LW UV exposure, long-term phosphorescence sometimes occurs at UV rather than visible light wavelengths, and can be detected photographically.

Gadolinium gallium garnet (GGG)

This has a pale straw-coloured fluorescence under LW UV, which changes to a peach colour under SW UV. Under X-rays, GGG fluoresces lilac.

Hydrogrossular garnet ('Transvaal jade')

This exhibits a characteristic orange glow under X-ray excitation, which serves to distinguish it from idocrase and the jade minerals.

Kunzite

This gemstone glows orange or gold under LW UV. Under X-rays the stone fluoresces a strong orange, and its body colour changes temporarily to a bluish-green.

Lapis lazuli

As this is a rock containing a mixture of minerals, its fluorescence tends to be patchy. Under LW UV spots and streaks of orange fluorescence are visible.

Opal

Natural opals may show a white, bluish, brownish or greenish fluorescence under LW UV, often with a persistent green phosphorescence. Synthetic opal shows no phosphorescence.

Paste

This is generally inert under LW UV, but glows a bright pale blue or green under SW UV.

Ruby

Both natural and synthetic rubies glow with a strong red fluorescence under LW UV, SW UV, and X-ray irradiation, the fluorescence of the synthetic stone being the stronger in each case. Unlike the natural gem, synthetic ruby shows a phosphorescent effect after exposure to X-rays.

Sapphire

Under LW UV, natural white sapphires generally fluoresce orange, but show no reaction under SW UV. Yellow sapphires from Sri Lanka glow a characteristic apricot yellow under LW UV, which distinguishes them from synthetic yellow corundum which is inert, and synthetic orange corundum which glows a strong red. Yellow sapphires from Australia and Thailand do not fluoresce at all, nor do any natural blue sapphires (due to the presence of iron), but synthetic blue sapphires show a strong greenish-blue fluorescence under SW UV due to the presence of titanium and a lack of iron. Because of their low iron content, blue Sri Lankan sapphires may also show a green fluorescence under SW UV.

Scapolite

This fluoresces yellow under LW UV and pink under SW UV.

Scheelite

Under SW UV this gem fluoresces blue, but is inert under LW UV.

Spinel

Green and yellow synthetic spinels, which contain manganese as their colouring element, show a bright green fluorescence under LW UV. Blue synthetic spinels (containing cobalt) fluoresce red under LW UV. Natural dark blue spinels (containing iron) do not fluoresce at all. Under SW UV, white synthetic spinels glow a strong blue/white in contrast to their lack of fluorescence under LW UV. Like ruby, red and pink (natural and synthetic) spinels glow bright red under LW and SW UV.

Strontium titanate

This man-made gem shows no reaction to any of the three types of irradiation.

Yttrium aluminium garnet (YAG)

Under LW UV and X-rays, this man-made gemstone shows a yellow fluorescence.

Zirconia (cubic zirconium oxide)

No fluorescence occurs under LW UV, but under SW UV American-made material (stabilised with yttrium oxide) fluoresces a very faint greenish-yellow, while Swiss-Austrian- and Russian-made material (stabilised with calcium oxide) glows a distinct yellow. All materials show a distinct whitish fluorescence under X-ray irradiation.

Electrical properties

Most gemstones are electrical insulators, but there are a few which are electrically conductive, and which will pass a current if a voltage is applied across them (*Figure 9.3*). The semiconductor properties of natural blue diamonds have already been mentioned, and are due to the presence of boron.

Another electrical property possessed by some minerals and in particular by tourmaline, is the *pyroelectric* effect. When pyroelectric materials are heated, they develop an electric charge across the opposite ends of the crystal axis. Tourmaline and quartz exhibit *piezoelectric* properties and become charged when stressed in certain directions.

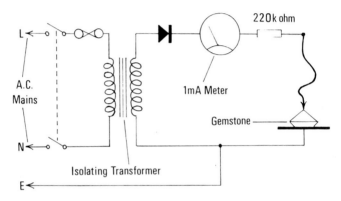

Fig. 9.3. A test circuit for checking the electrical conductivity of gemstones. This can be used to distinguish natural blue semi-conductor diamonds from diamonds which have been coloured blue artificially

Some materials (like diamond) are *photoconductive*, and their normally high electrical resistance falls when they are exposed to ultraviolet light. Semiconductor diamonds containing boron atoms are also photoconductive to gamma radiation, and are used (like a geiger tube) as radioactive counters in situations which call for a strong corrosion-resistant sensor material.

Amber (and certain of its plastic simulants) is a *triboelectric* material, which develops a negative electrostatic charge on its surface when rubbed. In this state it is capable of picking up small fragments of paper.

10 Organic Gem Materials and their Simulants

Organic gem materials are those which have been produced by living organisms. With the exception of pearl and coral, these materials are all amorphous substances, in contrast to the inorganic gem minerals which have a crystalline structure.

Pearls

Despite their softness and their vulnerability to acid attack, perspiration and cosmetics, pearls have managed to maintain their status as one of the most popular of the gems. Like other valuable gems, 'native' or natural pearls have many simulants. These can be divided into two broad groups: cultured pearls and imitation pearls. Although both natural and cultured pearls can easily be distinguished from the imitations, one of the more difficult tasks facing the gemmologist and jeweller has been the separation of the natural pearl from the cultured product.

The natural pearl is formed inside a mollusc as the result of a foreign substance penetrating the creature's shell and setting up an irritation. The mollusc reacts by surrounding the intruder (which may be a grain of sand or a parasite) with a 'sac' of mantle from its protective inner coating, and this in turn secretes a deposit which encapsulates the 'intruder' with concentric layers of nacre.

The nacreous deposit consists of a very thin network of conchiolin cells whose interstices are filled with minute crystals of aragonite. These crystals are an orthorhombic form of calcite ($CaCO_3$) and are orientated with their principal axes at right-angles to the layer. Once the original source of irritation is covered with nacre, the mollusc continues depositing further layers for up to seven years, the thousands of thin translucent layers eventually forming a pearl.

Although most molluscs have the ability to produce pearls in this manner, the main source of these gems is the *pinctada* salt-water species. These molluscs live in warm shallow seas, and are harvested for their pearl content in many locations including the Persian Gulf, Sri Lanka, Tahiti, the north-west coast of Australia and the coast of southern Burma.

The formation of the pearl within the mollusc can result either from the 'intruder' becoming embedded in the layer of mantle to produce a *cyst* pearl, or from it attaching itself to the nacreous surface of the shell to produce a *blister* pearl. While the cyst pearl is a completely formed and usually spherical pearl, the blister pearl has to be cut out of the mollusc's shell, and is therefore not completely formed. With blister pearls, the part which was joined to the shell is not covered with nacre. Because of this, it is usually smoothed off and then hidden by the jewellery setting.

The main attraction of the pearl lies in its iridescent sheen. This is caused by a combination of interference and diffraction effects in the thin surface layers of the gem, and is called the pearl's *orient*. Although the majority of gem quality pearls have a silver-white lustre, pearls found in the Gulf of Mexico are black, and their colour is said to be caused by the content of the sea water. Pink pearls are found in a univalve mollusc called the 'great conch' off the coasts of Florida and the West Indies.

Fresh-water pearls are produced by various clam and mussel species, and are found mainly in rivers in the UK and North America. Pearls have hardnesses in the range 3.5 to 4.0 on the Mohs scale, specific gravities between 2.6 and 2.8, and refractive indices from 1.52 to 1.66 (1.53 to 1.69 for black pearls).

Cultured pearls

Cultured salt-water pearls are produced by inserting a mother-of-pearl bead and a small fragment of mantle into an incision cut in the shell of a three-year old mollusc. The mollusc is then placed in a cage and returned to the sea. Three years later, the mollusc is removed from the sea once again, and the mother-of-pearl bead, now transformed into a cultured pearl with a 1 to 2 mm layer of nacre, is extracted.

Cultured blister pearls, known as *Mabe* pearls, are produced by cementing a small pellet of mother-of-pearl to the inside surface of the mollusc's shell. The mollusc is then returned to the sea where the pellet becomes covered with a layer of nacre. After two or three years, the mollusc is recovered and the resulting blister pearl is sawn out of its shell. A piece of polished mother-of-pearl is then cemented to the base of the pearl to form a fully rounded gem.

In a later production method, a soft bead is used in place of the mother-of-pearl pellet. After the blister pearl has been cut from the shell, this bead is removed, the cavity is cleaned out (and sometimes tinted), and a smaller glass bead is cemented in its place. The base of the blister pearl is then covered as before with a polished piece of mother-of-pearl.

Non-nucleated pearls

It is now known that pearl formation will occur if just the fragment of mantle is inserted into the mollusc. However, the size of the resulting pearl is smaller as it is almost entirely composed of deposited layers of nacre. Non-nucleated pearls of this type, known as *Biwa* pearls, are farmed round the shores of lake Biwa in Japan. These are cultured pearls which are produced in the large fresh-water clam *Hyriopsis Schlegeli*. Apart from the absence of solid bead nuclei (which were not successful when used in this variety of mollusc), the main difference between fresh-water farming on lake Biwa and the methods used for salt-water culturing is the simultaneous production of more than one pearl in each clam.

The mantle of the clam is notched in several places, and a small piece of mantle is inserted into each cut. The clam is then returned to the water for a period of three years, and after the pearls have been harvested from it. it is then returned to the water, when a second crop may sometimes occur naturally. The first crop of pearls are usually oval or baroque in shape, and as a result of the absence of a bead are small (less than five grains in weight). Because of their shape and size, they are often re-inserted as 'seeds' into another clam to produce a second crop of larger pearls having a better shape.

Distinguishing natural from cultured pearls

The identification of natural and cultured pearls can be difficult, as both have surface coatings of the same material. To the experienced pearl dealer, the subtle differences between the two types of pearl often provide enough clues for a positive identification. For example, the more translucent outer coating of the cultured pearl gives it a waxy lustre, and its surface is generally smoother and more regular than that of the natural pearl. With drilled pearls, if the drill hole is inspected with a hand lens it is often possible to see the sharp boundary between the bead nucleus and the outer coating of the cultured version. Beyond this boundary there is also a complete absence of growth lines.

A technique called 'candling' can also reveal the difference between cultured and natural pearls. To make this test, the pearl is rotated slowly in front of a strong light which is completely masked except for a 1 mm square test aperture. If the pearl is a cultured one, the structure of the mother-of-pearl bead will be projected onto its surface as parallel lines. If the pearls are in a necklace, they can be tested by stretching the necklace taut between its two ends and rotating it under a strong light. If any of the pearls are cultured, the internal bead will reflect the light through the nacreous covering, producing two gleams or flashes of light for each complete rotation of the pearl.

The mother-of-pearl bead forming the nucleus of the cultured pearl has a greater specific gravity than the natural pearl, and this makes possible another simple test. If the pearls are placed in a heavy liquid which has been adjusted to the

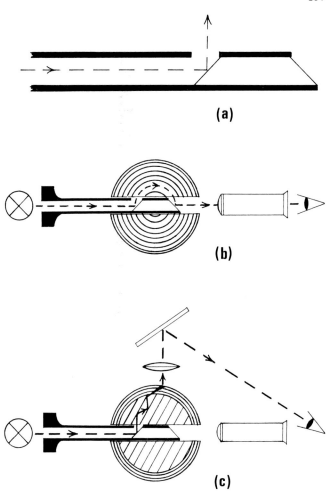

Fig. 10.1. The construction of the endoscope needle is shown at (a). Light is channelled round the concentric layers of a natural pearl to produce a flash of light in the viewing microscope (b). With a cultured nucleated pearl, the light escapes through the mother-of-pearl bead, and can be seen as a line of light on the pearl's surface (c)

specific gravity of calcite (i.e. bromoform diluted with monobromonaphthalene to an SG of 2.71), the majority of natural
pearls will float, while the majority of cultured pearls will sink.

Two further tests, which give a more reliable identification,
will now be described. The first of these uses an instrument
called an *endoscope*. This was originally manufactured in France,
but because of the decline in the importance of the natural
pearl, is now no longer available. The endoscope consists of a
hollow needle over which the pearl is threaded. The needle
contains, at its far end, a short metal rod whose end faces are
polished to an angle of $45°$ to form two mirror surfaces (*Figure
10.1(a)*). The needle has a hole cut in it immediately in front
of the rod, and this allows light which is injected down the
needle to be reflected out of the hole and into the pearl.

The pearl under test is moved carefully to and fro along
the needle while viewing the output end of the needle through
a microscope. If the pearl is a natural one, a position can be
found where light from the hole in the needle is channelled
round the concentric layers of the pearl and is reflected by the
second mirror surface into the microscope as a flash of light
(*Figure 10.1(b)*). If, however, the pearl is a cultured one, no
flash of light can be seen in any position. If the pearl is then
rotated on the needle, light rays will pass through the parallel
layers of the mother-of-pearl nucleus and appear as a line of
light on the outside surface of the pearl. A lens and a mirror
are fitted to the endoscope to enable the operator to view this
effect from the microscope position (*Figure 10.1(c)*).

More recently, a thin glass-fibre light guide coupled to a
strong light source has been used as a method of illuminating
the inside of the pearl drill hole.

The other confirmatory pearl test depends on the use of
X-ray equipment. The technique, while not normally in the
province of the gemmologist and jeweller, is however available
in the more specialised gem testing laboratory, and is described
here for the sake of completeness.

In natural pearls, the aragonite crystals are aligned radially
round the pearl with their major axes at right-angles to the surface. When the pearl is placed in a narrow beam of X-rays,

these crystals scatter some of the rays and produce a *Laue* diffraction pattern of spots which can be recorded on a photographic film. Because of the atomic structure within the aragonite crystals, this diffraction pattern will have a hexagonal symmetry for any orientation of the natural pearl (*Figure 10.2 (a)*).

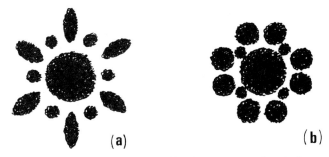

(a)   (b)

Fig. 10.2. The hexagonal Laue diffraction pattern produced when a narrow beam of X-rays penetrates a natural pearl is shown at (a). With a cultured nucleated pearl, both the hexagonal pattern and the four-point pattern shown at (b) can be produced, depending on the orientation of the bead

With the nucleated cultured pearl, this hexagonal pattern is only produced in one position where the crystals in the mother-of-pearl bead are parallel to the line of the X-rays. In all other positions of the pearl a four-point symmetry pattern is produced (*Figure 10.2(b)*). If the first X-ray diffraction picture of the pearl under test shows hexagonal symmetry, a second exposure is taken with the pearl rotated through 90°. If this also produces a hexagonal pattern, then the pearl is a natural one. With cultured pearls, the odds are against it being randomly aligned in the hexagonal position, and the diagnostic four-point symmetry pattern is usually produced on the first exposure.

One problem with the X-ray diffraction test is that if the pearls are part of a necklace, they must be unstrung so that the individual pearls can be tested in both orientations. However, with careful adjustment of exposure levels and exposure times, it is now possible to take a contact X-ray picture, or radiograph, of a complete string of pearls by broadening the X-ray beam. This produces a clear picture of the difference in X-ray transparency between the outer layers of a cultured pearl and its mother-of-pearl or glass bead nucleus. With a natural pearl, the transparency varies more evenly with the thickness of the pearl, and several fine concentric growth lines are usually visible.

With non-nucleated pearls, X-ray radiography reveals tell-tale small irregular hollows or patches near the centres which are completely dissimilar to the circular, often banded, structure seen in the centres of natural pearls. Biwa pearls, in common with most fresh-water pearls, contain traces of manganese which cause them to fluoresce under X-ray irradiation. After being irradiated, Biwa pearls show a persistent phosphorescence which helps in their identification.

Imitation pearls

Imitation or paste pearls fall into three main categories: solid glass spheres, mother-of-pearl spheres, and hollow glass spheres filled with wax. All three of these are given a lustrous outer coating by dipping them in a preparation called *essence d'orient*. This is a paste made from the scales of a fish called the *bleak*. Alternatively, hollow spheres may be coated on the inside with *essence d'orient* before being filled with wax. In the better quality imitations, several coatings of essence are applied, and the beads are dipped in clear cellulose acetate and then in cellulose nitrate to produce a light-interference effect.

Imitation pearls can best be detected by inspecting the edges of the drill holes, as there will usually be chips visible in the coating, or some indication of the underlying glass surface. Under the microscope (at 40 to 100× magnification), the typical paralleled edges of the overlapping layers of nacre seen on the surface of natural and cultured pearls will be absent from the imitation gem. A needle inserted at an angle into the drill hole can be used to detect the soft wax filling of the hollow-sphere variety.

Black pearls from the Gulf of Mexico often have their colour enhanced by being stained with silver nitrate. This tends to produce an unnaturally even and intense black coating, which is noticeably different from the more bronze or greyish iridescent shades of the untreated pearl, Black pearls fluoresce a faint red under crossed filters or LW UV, and this effect is completely suppressed when they are stained with silver nitrate. Imitation black pearls in the form of polished beads of haematite are lacking in the iridescent lustre typical of the genuine article. Haematite imitations can also be distinguished by their high specific gravity (5.1).

Mother-of-pearl and cameos

Mother-of-pearl is obtained from the iridescent nacreous layers deposited on the smooth inside surface of mollusc shells. Like the pearl, this iridescence is due to interference and diffraction effects caused by the thin overlapping layers of nacre. Some shells, such as the ear-shaped abalone variety, are particularly beautiful, and have coloured banded growth contours (*Figure 10.3*).

Fig. 10.3. Three cultured pearls on a piece of shaped abalone shell

Fig. 10.4. A cameo carved from a piece of shell

Cameos are cut from shells (and agates) having two or more layers of contrasting shade or colour. The uppermost layer is carved into a relief figure or design, while the underlying layer is exposed to form the background colour (*Figure 10.4*).

Amber

This is a fossilised form of pine resin, which was originally extruded from conifer trees some thirty to sixty million years ago in the Eocene and Palaeocene periods.

The Greeks gave amber the name *electrum* (i.e. 'sun-made'). Subsequently amber was found to produce a negative electrostatic charge when rubbed, and to be capable of picking up small pieces of paper (an ability shared by several of its plastic imitations). Because of its initial association with amber, this phenomenon gave rise to the word 'electricity' which was coined from the Greek 'electrum'.

Amber is usually a pale yellow-brown translucent material, but reddish-brown, greenish-brown and black varieties are also found occasionally. Sea amber is recovered from the shores of the Baltic (where it is known as the 'gold of the Baltic') and from the coastline of Sicily. Pit amber is mined principally in Palmnicken, near Kaliningrad, USSR, although a less important source exists in Romania.

Pieces of amber which are large enough for fashioning into gems or ornaments are called *block* amber. Smaller pieces of acceptable quality are heated to about 180°C and compressed

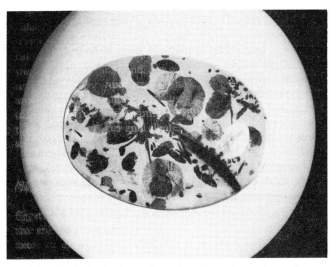

Fig. 10.5. Cracks in the form of circular iridescent spangles can be seen in this piece of amber which has been clarified by heating it in rape seed oil

together (or extruded through sieves) to form *reconstructed* or *pressed* amber (also known as 'ambroid'). This can be distinguished from block amber by its 'frozen' viscous appearance, by the boundaries of different colour and clarity, and by the bubble inclusions, which are elongated instead of rounded. Cloudy amber is sometimes cleared by heating it in rape seed oil. The oil penetrates the bubbles, which are the cause of the cloudiness, and makes them transparent. The process often produces circular cracks in the form of iridescent spangles, which enhance the appearance of the amber (*Figure 10.5*).

Among the many amber imitations, perhaps the most convincing is *copal resin* which is derived from various tropical trees, and is the basis for copal varnish. Unfortunately, copal has a similar specific gravity to amber (1.10) and cannot be distinguished from it by hydrostatic weighing or immersion in salt solution. Unlike amber, however, copal softens in ether, and a small drop of the fluid will leave a dull spot on its surface. Copal also crumbles readily under the knife blade, and when fractured its surface is characteristically 'crazed' with a network of fine cracks.

Glass imitations of amber are easily detected because of their hardness (5.0 to 6.0 compared with amber's 2.5), and the fact that they are colder to the touch. Glass can also be separated from amber, as can many of the plastic imitations, by a specific gravity test.

A suitable 'heavy liquid' for testing amber can be made up by dissolving ten level teaspoons of common salt in a half-pint of water. This produces a solution having a specific gravity of approximately 1.13. Amber (and copal resin) has a specific gravity of 1.10, and will float in the salt solution, but glass and plastic imitations, such as Bakelite and casein, will sink. Amber has a refractive index of 1.54.

Ivory

Elephant tusks are a well-known source of dentine ivory, but ivory is also obtained from the tusks of the walrus and the hippopotamus, from the front teeth of the narwhal (a dolphin-like arctic mammal), and, more rarely, from the tusks of fossilised mammoths. A form of vegetable ivory is produced by the hard white kernal of the corozo nut, which is the fruit of the ivory nut palm.

Dentine ivory may sometimes include some enamel and other organic substances. It is a relatively soft substance (2.0 to 3.0) and has a splintery fracture. The best quality ivory comes from the tusks of the Indian elephant, which are smaller than those of the African elephant. Mammoth ivory from the Russian Urals and Siberia is harder than other varieties of ivory, but is usually flawed by cracks. The refractive index of ivory is in the region of 1.54, and its specific gravity lies between 1.7 and 2.0.

Ivory imitations include many plastics, the most convincing being celluloid. This is less dense than ivory (SG of 1.3 to 1.8), and unlike ivory it can be pared with a knife. Bone is another material used to imitate ivory, but has a greater specific gravity (1.9 to 2.1), and under the microscope, bone peelings show a multitude of *Haversian Canals* that may resemble a bull's-eye or wavy canals (at higher magnification, the bone cells resemble the shape of an outspread spider). Ivory, when viewed under the microscope, shows wavy parallel lines like the growth contours in a section of tree trunk. This is an optical effect caused by the submicroscopic structure of the ivory. Vegetable ivory derived from the corozo nut is less dense than dentine ivory (SG of 1.4), and a peeling shows a pattern of interconnected oval cells.

Odontolite

Also known as *bone turquoise*, this is fossil bone or dentine ivory obtained from prehistoric animals such as the mammoth. It owes its blue colour to vivianite, an iron phosphate, and is used as a turquoise simulant. Under the microscope its organic structure is clearly visible. It is much more dense than ivory (SG of 3.0 to 3.25) and also harder (5.0).

Tortoiseshell

The main source of supply of tortoiseshell material is not the tortoise, but the outer shell or scale of the Hawksbill sea turtle. The individual plates, or *blades*, of the turtle's shell are a mottled yellow-brown; the front blades are called *shoulder plates*, the centre ones *cross-backs*, the side ones *main plates*, and the rear ones *tail plates*. A clear yellow tortoiseshell is obtained from the turtle's under-shell.

The refractive index of tortoiseshell is in the region of 1.55, and its specific gravity is about 1.3. Like amber, small pieces can be softened by heating (to $100\,^\circ$C) and moulded together to form more usable sizes.

Various plastics, including casein, are used to imitate tortoiseshell. These can be distinguished from the genuine material by the nature of the body colour. In tortoiseshell, this can be seen to be made up of small discs of pigment when viewed under the microscope. The pigment in the various plastic imitations is either more homogeneous, or is distributed in the material as bands or swirls of colour.

Jet

Often used as beads in Victorian mourning jewellery (*Figure 10.6*), this material is once again becoming fashionable. Jet, a variety of fossilised wood, similar to lignite or brown coal, is halfway in formation between peat and bituminous coal. It has a hardness of 3.5, a specific gravity of 1.3 and a refractive index in the region of 1.66. During Victorian times a rich source of jet was found near Whitby in Yorkshire. The main sources of the material now are Spain, France and Utah in the USA.

The five main simulants of jet are black pressed amber, black stained chalcedony, vulcanite (a hard black vulcanised rubber also known as ebonite), gutta percha and a moulded glass known as 'French jet' or 'Vauxhall' glass. Amber can easily be distinguished from jet by its low specific gravity, and chalcedony can be identified by its greater hardness and density. If touched with a hot needle, or worked with a file, vulcanite gives off a

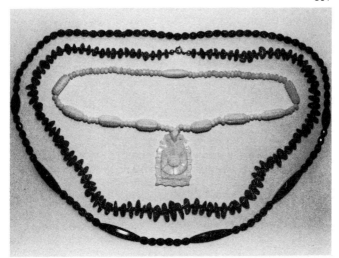

Fig. 10.6. Three necklaces made from bone, amber and jet

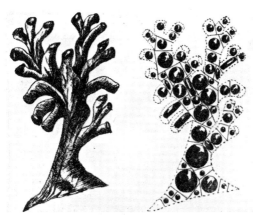

Fig. 10.7 Growth of coral and showing the way beads are cut from the 'tree'

rubber smell. French jet has an 'orange peel' texture, and often contains bubbles typical of glass.

Coral

This is another popular Victorian gem material which is coming back into fashion. Coral is composed mainly of calcium carbonate ($CaCO_3$). Its branching plant-like structure (*Figure 10.7*) is formed by the skeletal remains of various types of marine polyp which live in colonies in shallow subtropical waters. *Precious coral* is the rose tinted variety used in necklaces, in bracelets and occasionally in cameos. White coral is sometimes stained to produce the more valuable rose pink variety.

Natural coral can be distinguished from its imitations by its cellular structure, and by the fact that the application of a small drop of hydrochloric acid causes it to effervesce. It has a hardness of 3.5 to 4.0, and its specific gravity ranges from 1.34 for the black variety, to 2.6–2.7 for the white and pink varieties.

11 Synthetic Gemstones

For the purposes of gemmology, a *synthetic* is defined as a subtance which has been produced artificially, and which has the same chemical composition, crystal structure and physical properties as its natural counterpart. Synthetic gemstones, which are exact copies of naturally occuring mineral substances, fit this definition, but many crystalline products have been made which do not exist in nature, and these are more accurately described as 'man-made', rather than synthetic. To complete the picture, a gemstone *simulant* need only have the outward appearance of the object it imitates. Confusion between the terms 'synthetic' and 'simulant' often results in the description 'synthetic diamond' being applied to a diamond simulant, particularly where this happens to be a man-made or a synthetic substance (i.e. a YAG or a synthetic corundum).

The French chemist Frémy produced the first commerical synthetic gemstones in 1877. These were small ruby crystals and were grown by fusing together a mixture containing alumina in a clay crucible, the process taking some eight days. In 1885, larger 'synthetic' rubies made their appearance. At the time, these were thought to have been made by fusing together smaller fragments of natural gemstone, and because of this they were called *reconstructed* rubies. These 'synthetic' gems contained many bubbles, together with what appeared to be strongly marked curved growth lines. More recent analysis of surviving specimens has indicated that the rubies were probably manufactured by an early form of *flame fusion* process, using alumina powder rather than fragments of ruby. The fact that the sintering, or fusing together, of ruby fragments would almost certainly have destroyed their colour also adds weight to the theory that flame fusion was the more likely method of manufacture.

As we have already begun to use terms such as 'flame fusion' to describe the early attempts at gemstone synthesis, this is a good point at which to integrate the history of synthetic gemstone production with descriptions of the principal crystal growing techniques.

The Verneuil flame fusion process

This method was invented at the turn of the century by the French scientist M. A. Verneuil who, starting as an assistant to Frémy, devoted most of his life to the problems of corundum synthesis. Today, Verneuil furnaces are in use in many countries, including France, Germany, Switzerland, Austria, Japan and the USA. The furnace (*Figure 11.1*) consists basically of an inverted oxy-hydrogen blowpipe-type burner, a powder dispenser and a ceramic pedestal.

When corundum is being synthesised, the dispenser is filled with a high-purity alumina powder (Al_2O_3). This is produced by re-crystallising ammonium alum from solution in water until it is pure, and then calcining it in a furnace at $1100\,^{\circ}$C. The calcining operation drives off the ammonia and sulphur dioxide gases to leave pure *gamma* alumina. The appropriate colouring impurity is added to the alum before it is calcined (e.g. chromic oxide for ruby, titanium and iron oxides for blue sapphire, nickel oxide for yellow sapphire, manganese for pink sapphire, copper for bluish-green sapphire, cobalt for dark blue sapphire and vanadium oxide, plus a trace of chromic oxide, for an 'alexandrite' colour change effect).

The alumina powder in the dispenser is automatically fed in carefully controlled doses through the blowpipe's central oxygen feed line. As the powder drops through the $2200\,^{\circ}$C oxy-hydrogen flame, it melts and falls onto the surface of the ceramic pedestal, which is enclosed in a circular firebrick chamber (*Figure 11.1*). When the molten alumina powder starts solidifying, the powder feed rate is increased until a

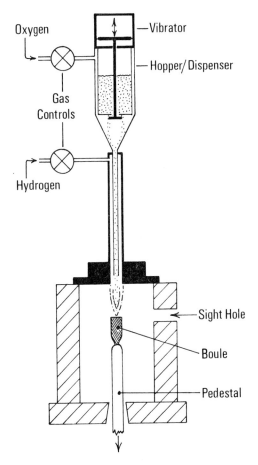

Fig. 11.1. The Verneuil furnace uses an inverted oxy-hydrogen burner to produce synthetic crystal boules by the flame fusion of powdered source material

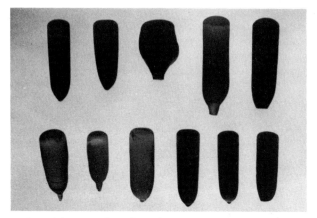

*Fig. 11.2. Examples of synthetic corundum and synthetic
spinel boules*

corundum *boule* of 15 to 25 mm diameter begins to form. As
the boule grows, the height of the pedestal is adjusted so that
the top section of the crystal is maintained in the hottest part
of the flame. A typical 40 to 80 mm long corundum boule
weighing between 200 and 500 carats will take about four
hours to grow (*Figure 11.2*).

The rapid growth and subsequent cooling of the boule
produces internal stresses which would cause it to crack if it
was sawn at right-angles to its major axis. Because of this, the
boule is split in half lengthwise to release these stresses after
its removal from the furnace. To obtain maximum yield, gems
are cut from these two halves with their major axis (i.e. girdle/
table facet) parallel to the length of the boule.

The first synthetic rubies produced by the Verneuil process
appeared in 1910. World production of Verneuil corundum is
now in excess of 1000 million carats a year, the bulk of this
being used for instrument bearings, watch bearings, the tips of
record player styli and as thread guides for the textile industry.

For many years it was thought that star rubies and sapphires
would never be reproduced in synthetic form. In 1947, however, the Linde Company of America began the commercial

manufacture of star corundums, and these are now also produced by companies in Germany and Japan. Titanium oxide is added to the alumina powder, and the synthetic corundum boule is grown in the normal way in a verneuil furnace. The finished boule is then heated again to precipitate out the titanium oxide as rutile needles along the line of the three lateral crystal axes.

Synthetic spinels were first produced by the Verneuil method in 1926, using a mixture of alumina and magnesia (MgO and Al_2O_3). Surprisingly, it has not been found possible to grow synthetic spinel boules successfully using a 1:1 mixture of these two constituents, and best quality boules are produced by using one part magnesia to three parts alumina (i.e. $MgO.3Al_2O_3$). The resulting boule contains a mixture of synthetic spinel and gamma alumina, and this causes strains within the material which show up as anomalous birefringence when it is viewed between crossed polarising filters (see under 'The polariscope' in Chapter 6).

The mixture of magnesia and alumina also makes the refractive index and specific gravity of the synthetic product significantly higher than that of natural spinel, and this enables the two materials to be easily distinguished from each other. Spinel boules differ physically from the rounded corundum crystals in that they usually have slightly flattened sides, which are the visible evidence of the material's cubic crystal system.

The main colouring agents employed in the production of synthetic spinels are cobalt oxide for blue stones, iron oxide for pink stones and manganese oxide for pale green stones. None of these colours resembles the tints seen in natural spinels, as it has not been found possible to reproduce these more delicate greyish shades. For this reason, most synthetic spinels are produced in colours which simulate those of other gemstones (e.g. aquamarine, sapphire and zircon). Red spinels have proved to be more difficult to manufacture by the Verneuil process (although crystals have been grown successfully by the flux melt method). The addition of chromic oxide results in a green spinel. However, red spinels have been made by the Verneuil process using chromic oxide in a 1:1 magnesia/alumina mix. Because the resulting boules crack easily, only small stones can be cut from them.

Synthetic rutile and strontium titanate, the latter having no natural counterpart, are also manufactured by the Verneuil process, but as the titanium constituent of both of these materials tends to lose its oxygen at temperatures close to its melting point, it is necessary to supply the boule with extra oxygen during its growth. This is done by replacing the standard Verneuil blowpipe with a *tricone* burner. This burner has an extra outer tube which is fed with a separate supply of oxygen and enriches the flame with an envelope of the gas. Even with the extra supply of oxygen, the finished boules are black in colour and have to be annealed in oxygen to make them transparent.

The Czochralski process

This is a crystal 'pulling' process commonly used for growing high purity material for the optical and laser industries. It uses a seed crystal which is dipped into a heated platinum crucible containing the molten source material. The seed is then very slowly raised out of the melt at a carefully controlled rate. The molten source material crystallises on the seed and grows downwards as it is slowly 'pulled' out of the crucible. The technique is used to grow large ruby crystals and rare earth garnets (YAG, YIG, etc.) for use in lasers. It is also used to produce synthetic scheelite, fluorspar, lithium niobate and, more recently, the alexandrite variety of chrysoberyl.

The Bridgeman—Stockbarger process

In this method, the source material is placed in a crucible in the upper part of a vertical furnace. When the material has become molten, the crucible is slowly moved into the cooler lower section of the furnace, and crystals begin to grow in the melt as its temperature drops. The process was developed to manu-facture laser materials and other specialised crystals. Gemstone materials, including scheelite and fluorite, have since been produced as by-products.

The 'skull' crucible process

Because of the high melting point of zirconia powder (used in the production of the diamond simulant, cubic zirconium oxide) crystals of this material are grown by means of a *skull* melting technique which was originated in the Lebedev Physical Institute, Moscow. The process uses a cold 'skull' crucible, and the melt is contained within a crust formed from the zirconia powder. The crucible consists of a cylindrical arrangement of water-cooled copper 'fingers'.

The zirconia powder (plus a stabiliser to maintain the cubic crystal formation of the material as it cools) is melted within the crucible by means of radio-frequency (RF) heating induced from a surrounding copper coil. As zirconia powder is an insulator at room temperatures, and cannot therefore be heated by the radio frequency field from cold, pieces of zirconium metal are added to the powder. These heat up rapidly and raise the temperature of the powder to a point where it becomes electrically conductive and can then be melted by the RF field.

The bulk of the zirconia powder melts, except for a thin layer next to the cooled copper tubes, and this layer acts as a high-temperature crucible for the molten zirconia. After some hours, the RF heating power is slowly reduced, and cubic zirconium oxide crystals form as the melt cools. Coloured zirconia crystals can be grown by introducing various additives to the powder.

The hydrothermal process

Unlike the Verneuil, Czochralski, Bridgeman–Stockbarger and 'skull' crucible processes, which are used to grow crystals direct from the molten material, the hydrothermal method grows crystals from an aqueous solution of the source material. If water is heated under pressure, its temperature can be raised well above its normal boiling point of $100\,^{\circ}$C. At 100 atmosphere pressure, the boiling point of water is $400\,^{\circ}$C, and at this temperature water acts as a solvent for many minerals including quartz.

The hydrothermal process uses the solubility of source materials in superheated water to produce a supersaturated aqueous solution from which gem crystals can be precipitated onto a suitable seed. To grow quartz crystals, slightly alkaline water (containing one per cent by volume of sodium hydroxide) is placed in a pressure vessel called an *autoclave* (*Figure 11.3*).

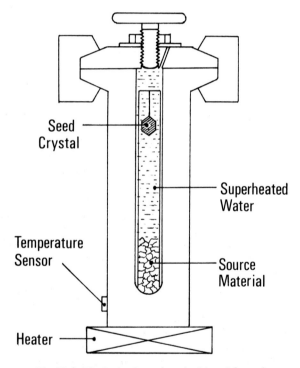

Fig. 11.3. The hydrothermal method is mainly used to grow synthetic quartz (for the electronics industry) and synthetic emerald. Source material is dissolved in superheated water in an autoclave and re-crystallised onto a seed

Crushed quartz crystals are placed at the bottom of the auto-clave as the source material, and slices of quartz are hung in the water to act as seeds. The vessel is then sealed and the heater energised. When the temperature in the bottom of the autoclave reaches the region of $400\,^{\circ}C$, the crushed quartz crystals dissolve in the water and the silica-rich solution begins to rise.

The temperature of the water in the region of the seeds is about $40\,^{\circ}C$ lower than at the base of the autoclave, and when the silica solution reaches this cooler area it becomes super-saturated and crystallises out on the seed plates. Quartz crystals up to 50 mm in diameter and 150 mm long can be grown in three to four weeks by this method. Synthetic coloured quartz for use in jewellery can be produced by adding cobalt (blue) or iron (green or yellow) to the solution. Synthetic emerald and ruby are also grown by the hydrothermal process. Synthetic amethyst is produced by adding iron and irradiating the crystal with a radioactive source.

In 1960, J. Lechleitner of Innsbruck, Austria, used the hydrothermal technique to deposit a thin coat of synthetic emerald onto an already faceted and polished beryl gemstone of poor colour.The crown facets of the coated stone were then lightly polished, but the pavilion facets were left in a matt condition to retain as much colour in the gemstone as possible. The emerald-coated beryl gemstones were first marketed under the name 'Emerita' (which was later changed to 'Symerald'), and were subsequently produced by the Linde company of America as 'Linde Synthetic Emerald'. More recently, the Lechleitner coated emerald has been marketed by Sturmlechner of Vienna. In 1964, J. Lechleitner produced hydrothermally grown synthetic emeralds from seed plates, and this was followed in 1965 by a similar product from Linde. Another synthetic emerald manufactured by the hydrothermal process, and owing its colour not to chromium (as in natural emerald) but to vanadium, was developed by the Crystals Research company of Melbourne, Australia. In 1979 yet another hydro-thermal emerald was introduced by the American company Vacuum Venture.

The flux melt process

This, like the hydrothermal method, is a solvent-based process. It was developed in 1935 by the German dye manufacturing company I. G. Farbenindustrie, for the purpose of producing synthetic emerald. The method uses a heated platinum crucible (*Figure 11.4*) in which the constituent gem materials (beryllium and aluminium oxides, plus chromium as a colouring agent) are dissolved in a lithium molybdate solvent at about $800\,^\circ C$. Slabs of silica glass are floated on top of the melt, and the beryllium and aluminium oxides combine with them to form a beryl solution. Seed crystals of natural or synthetic beryl are then lowered into the solution on a platinum frame, and the temperature of the crucible is slowly reduced to a pre-set level. As the beryl solution becomes supersaturated, crystals of synthetic emerald are precipitated out of the solution and

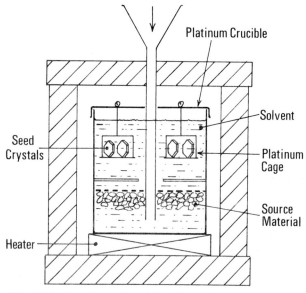

Fig. 11.4. The flux melt method is used to grow synthetic emerald crystals from source material dissolved in lithium molybdate

grow on the seeds. The process is a very slow one, requiring accurate temperature stabilisation to produce the correct thermal gradient in the crucible. It is also necessary to replenish the source materials at regular intervals to maintain the growth of the crystals.

In 1939 the war interrupted the work of the German company and their 'Igmerald' synthetic emerald was never produced commercially. In 1940, the American chemist C. F. Chatham also succeeded in synthesising emerald. The process was kept secret, but the Chatham emeralds were close enough in character to the German Igmerald to indicate that they were also a product of a flux melt process. In 1963, Pierre Gilson in France further improved the flux melt technique to produce high-quality Gilson emeralds. Another synthetic emerald grown by the flux melt method was introduced by W. Zerfass of Idar-Oberstein, Germany.

As already mentioned, the process of crystal growth by the flux melt method is a very slow one, and takes between six and ten months to produce a crystal of suitable size for cutting. In this respect it closely mirrors the geological process of gemstone formation, rapid cooling producing a multitude of tiny crystals, and the production of large crystals requiring a very slow and steady precipitation.

Synthetic ruby, spinel, quartz, alexandrite and the rare earth garnets are also produced by this method using the appropriate solvent and constituent materials.

Synthetic diamond production

The first authenticated synthetic diamonds were produced in 1953 by the Swedish ASEA company. Their aim was to make gem size stones, and not realising the importance of the industrial market for grit size diamonds, they kept their success in this field secret until after the American G. E. company had announced its own synthesis of diamond grits in 1955. Four years later, De Beers also successfully synthesised grit size diamonds, and using ASEA high-pressure presses developed their method into a commercial process.

The basic technique used in the large-scale synthesis of industrial diamond involves the dissolving of graphite in molten iron or nickel at high pressures and temperatures. In this process the metal acts as a catalyst to convert the loose hexagonal atomic structure of graphite into the compact cubic structure of diamond. The conversion is effected by applying pressure in the region of 110 000 atmospheres to a cartridge containing alternate discs of graphite and nickel, and at the same time heating these components by means of an electric current to 3300 °C. The nickel discs melt, dissolving the graphite and, as the temperature falls, cause it to re-crystallise as clusters of tiny synthetic diamonds. The process takes two to three minutes, and after the solidified metallic mass is removed from the press it is crushed, and the diamonds are extracted from it by dissolving away the non-diamond content with acids.

In 1970 synthetic gem quality carat-size diamonds were grown under laboratory conditions by the American G. E. company. These were produced by a diffusion technique in which free carbon atoms were persuaded to crystallise on synthetic diamond 'seeds'. The resulting tabular shaped diamonds were very expensive to produce in comparison with natural stones, and were therefore not economically viable as a commercial product. In 1971, Russian research workers announced that they had also synthesised gem diamond crystals, but they too decided that the production of gem quality synthetic diamonds were not an economic proposition.

Synthetic industrial diamonds are distinguishable from natural stones mainly by the fact that in their rapid crystal growth the nitrogen atoms present as impurities have had no time to aggregate into platelets, but are dispersed throughout the crystal lattice. All synthetically produced industrial stones therefore tend to be type Ib diamonds, and can be identified by their paramagnetic property (i.e. they are attracted by a magnet) which is due to traces of the catalyst.

With the laboratory-grown gem quality synthetic stones, nitrogen was excluded during their growth to produce the colourless type II diamond. Unlike natural diamonds, the colourless synthetic ones fluoresced strongly under SW UV, and showed a persistent phosphorescence. They were also identifiable by their semiconductor property which is only present in natural blue diamonds.

Distinguishing synthetic from natural gemstones

Because of the large difference in price between synthetic and natural gemstones, it is important that the gemmologist is not only able to identify the mineral species to which a stone belongs but is also able to determine whether it is a natural or a synthetic product. Gemstones which are used simply as simulants of other stones can be identified relatively easily by techniques already described in this book as their physical characteristics will differ from those of the gemstone they imitate. However, synthetic copies of naturally occurring gemstones (e.g. emerald, ruby, sapphire, alexandrite and opal) pose a more difficult problem, as their physical characteristics are often identical to those of the natural stone.

Identification of these stones is based on tell-tale indications within the gem of the very different ways in which the natural and synthetic crystals have grown. These include growth bands, colour zoning and various other internal features, all of which can be used to separate the natural from the synthetic gemstone. The most useful of these indicators are directly connected with the immediate environment in which the crystal grew.

Natural stones, crystallising slowly out of the molten magma in the earth's crust, were often 'host' to a variety of minute particles and crystals, which became trapped in the stone as *inclusions*.

These inclusions comprise three basic types; the first is called *pre-existing*, and consists of materials which were present before the host crystal began to form (e.g. solid particles and minute crystals). The second type is called *contemporary*, and consists of substances which occurred at the same time as the host crystal (e.g. droplets of the liquid from which the host crystal grew). The third type is called *post-contemporary*, and occurred after the formation of the host crystal (e.g.

various types of crack or fissure). Sometimes these inclusions are sufficiently characteristic to enable the gemstone's country of origin as well as its species to be identified. Synthetic gemstones, although much more free from extraneous inclusions than natural stones, also contain certain characteristic internal features, which range from bubbles or particles of unmelted powder to flaws and stresses.

The following notes list the principal identifying features used to distinguish natural from synthetic gems. To make comparison easier, the physical constants and typical inclusions of the natural stone are listed, where appropriate, for each of the species or varieties. As an additional aid, *Figure 11.5* contains sketches of a selection of typical internal features, and a list of inclusions appears at the end of Appendix A in this book. For a more detailed study of gemstone inclusions, reference should be made to B. W. Anderson's *Gem Testing*, and to E. Gübelin's *Internal World of Gemstones*.

Emerald

Characteristics of the natural gemstone:

$RI = 1.577$ to 1.583, $DR = 0.006$, $SG = 2.71$
Inclusions:

Brazil	Biotite mica. Thin films resembling paving stones.
Colombia (Chivor and Muzo mines)	Three-phase inclusions (*Figure 11.5(g)*).
India	Two-phase inclusions resembling 'Commas'.
Pakistan	Paving stone pattern of liquid inclusions. Phenakite inclusions.
Russia (Siberia)	Actinolite crystals in blade form.
Rhodesia (Sandawana)	Tremolite fibres. Transvaal mica.

Synthetic emeralds grown by the flux melt process (i.e. Chatham, Gilson and Zerfass products) generally have a lower

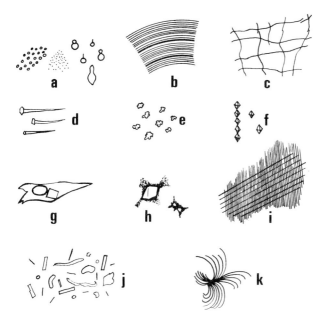

Fig. 11.5. Sketches of some of the more characteristic inclusions and growth features seen in synthetic and natural gemstones

(a) and (b) bubbles, powder and growth lines seen in some flame fusion synthetic corundums.

(c) Surface crazing seen in the hydrothermally deposited skin of Lechleitner emeralds.

(d) Phenakite crystals and conical voids forming nail-like inclusions in Linde hydrothermal emeralds.

(e) Breadcrumb-like inclusions in synthetic quartz.

(f) Octahedral crystals in natural spinel and sapphire.

(g) Three-phase inclusion (liquid, gas bubble, crystal), seen in Colombian emeralds.

(h) Zircon crystals surrounded by 'haloes', seen in Sri Lankan rubies and sapphires.

(i) Rutile needles seen as 'silk' in natural rubies and sapphires.

(j) Multitude of small transparent inclusions seen in hessonite garnet includes diopside and zircon crystals.

(k) 'Horsetail' inclusion of asbestos seen in demantoid garnet.

RI, birefringence and SG than natural emerald (RI = 1.560 to 1.563; DR = 0.003; SG = 2.65). Although iron oxide has been introduced experimentally into later Gilson emeralds to increase their SG (and to make the inclusions more like natural ones), this practice has probably been discontinued because the iron attacked the platinum seed holder.

If bromoform is diluted to an SG of 2.65 with rock crystal as an indicator, Chatham, Gilson and Zerfass emeralds will float within the liquid in the same manner as the indicator, but all natural emeralds will sink. Separation can also be made with a refractometer test, particularly if the more open scale of the spinel version is used.

A typical inclusion seen in these synthetics takes the form of a whispy veil or a curved lace-like feather (resembling thinly dispersed cigarette smoke).

Synthetic emeralds grown by the hydrothermal process (i.e. Lechleitner, Linde and Vacuum Venture products) have the same physical properties as natural emerald, and for their identification reliance has to be placed on the presence of growth features and inclusions. With both the Lechleitner and Linde 'coated' emerald, a network of fine cracks is often visible in the surface of the stone (*Figure 11.5(c)*). Parts of the pavilion may also be left in a matt unpolished condition in order not to weaken the colour. If the gemstone is immersed in bromoform, the dark rim of the emerald-coloured synthetic beryl can be seen. In the fully-hydrothermal Lechleitner, Linde and Vacuum Venture emeralds, it may be possible to see signs of the seed crystal, which is often lighter in colour. In addition to the lace-like feathers seen in other synthetic emeralds, the Linde product may show nail-like inclusions with the heads of the nails formed by phenakite crystals (*Figure 11.5(d)*). Linde emeralds also have a distinctive red fluorescence which is prominent enough to be seen in strong white light.

All synthetic emeralds are more transparent to SW UV light than are natural emeralds. This feature can be tested by the use of immersion contact photography. Using a darkened room, the unknown sample is placed on a piece of photographic paper together with a natural emerald as a reference. The paper is placed in the bottom of a shallow dish containing water, and is exposed to SW UV light for two to three seconds by holding the lamp some eighteen inches above the dish. If the photographic paper is then developed, and the exposure times have been correct, the reference emerald will appear white, and the unknown sample, if it is a synthetic, will appear black with a thin white rim round it.

Synthetic emeralds, being chromium rich and completely free from iron, fluoresce more strongly than natural emeralds under crossed filters, LW UV and SW UV. They also show a deeper red under the Chelsea colour filter (see Chapter 12).

Ruby

Characteristics of the natural gemstone:

RI = 1.764 to 1.772, DR = 0.008, SG = 3.99
Inclusions:

Burma	Calcite, zircon, spinel, rutile needles (star and silk – *Figure 11.5(i).*). 'Treacle' swirls of colour.
Thailand	Less inclusions than Burma. Garnet common (round opaque crystals surrounded by feathers).
Sri Lanka	Diffuse silk. Zircon crystals with 'haloes' (*Figure 11.5(h)*).

Synthetic rubies have exactly the same physical properties and constants as the natural stone, and the main identification features are those of growth lines and inclusions. They are principally manufactured by the Verneuil flame fusion process, although a few have been produced by the hydrothermal and flux melt methods (the latter including Kashan rubies).

Verneuil rubies sometimes contain gas bubbles (spherical and flask or tadpole-shaped) and clouds of unmelted powder (*Figure 11.5(a)*). The most prominent features, however, are the curved growth lines. These are best seen with the aid of a microscope, and when viewed in the right direction (and with the correct lighting), look like the parallel grooves on a gramophone record (*Figure 11.5(b)*). In natural rubies the growth lines are straight, and follow the hexagonal structure of the crystal.

Because of the way in which Verneuil rubies are cut from the boule (with the table orientated randomly to the main axis), dichroism is often visible through the table facet instead of through the girdle as in a natural stone.

In hydrothermal rubies, identification is more difficult, although it may be possible to see signs of the seed, and feathers typical of synthetic emerald may also be present. Feathers can sometimes be seen in flux melt rubies. In the Kashan variety, a typical dot-dash field of inclusions may be visible.

Synthetic rubies are more transparent to SW UV than natural ones, and the photographic immersion contact test described for emeralds can also be used for rubies.

Synthetic star rubies can generally be detected by eye, as the colour is much brighter and the star effect bolder and more sharply defined than in natural stones. Other characteristics seen in synthetic rubies are also applicable to the star variety.

Sapphire

Characteristics of the natural gemstone:

RI = 1.760 to 1.768, DR = 0.008, SG = 3.99
Inclusions:

Burma	Healing cracks (looking like crumpled flags). Short thick rutile needles.
Thailand	Never contains rutile. Crystals of plagioclase feldspar.
Sri Lanka	Feathers. Long thin rutile needles (long silk). Zircon crystals with 'haloes' (*Figure 11.5(h)*). Three-phase inclusions (*Figure 11.5(g)*). Rows of octahedral crystals.
India (*Kashmir*)	Cloudiness caused by very fine fissures.
USA (*Montana*)	Hexagonal crystals surrounded by liquid crystals.

As with ruby, synthetic sapphires have the same physical constants as the natural stone, and are mainly produced by the Verneuil process. The principal identification features of sapphires are colour zoning and inclusions. If a blue sapphire is placed in an immersion cell and covered with monobromonaphthalene (or even water), distinctive colour zoning can be seen when the stone is viewed in the right direction. In synthetic blue sapphires this zoning takes the form of curved lines of colour (*Figure 11.6*). In natural blue sapphires, the colour is much more patchy and the zoning consists of bands of colour following the hexagonal structure of the crystal (*Figure 11.7*).

The inclusions and growth lines to be found in synthetic sapphires are the same as those already described for rubies, although the sapphire growth lines are much more difficult to see, and are not present at all in yellow sapphires. Growth lines can often be enhanced by viewing the stone under SW UV light.

Like ruby, synthetic sapphires often show dichroism through the table facet, instead of through the girdle as with

Fig. 11.6. Curved colour zoning in synthetic blue sapphire

natural stones. There are also significant differences between the absorption spectra of synthetic and natural sapphires. Most natural stones contain iron, and this can be seen as three bands at 450, 460 and 471 nm (except for Sri Lankan stones which only show a faint band at 450 nm). Synthetic blue sapphires contain virtually no iron, and none of these bands are visible. In synthetic green and yellow sapphires, which are coloured with nickel, the three iron bands are also absent. Yellow sapphires from Sri Lanka show none of the three iron bands, but these can be easily distinguished from synthetic yellow sapphires as they fluoresce a distinctive apricot yellow under LW UV light, in contrast to the synthetic stones which are completely inert. Orange synthetic sapphires fluoresce red under LW UV.

Natural blue sapphires are inert under SW UV (except for an occasional Sri Lankan stone which may show a weak green fluorescence). Synthetic blue sapphires, because of their lack of iron, fluoresce a strong greenish-blue under SW UV.

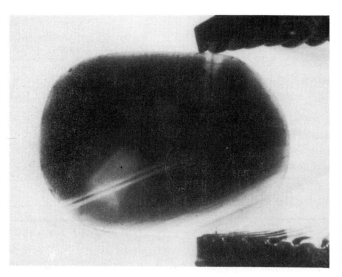

Fig. 11.7. Parallel colour zoning bands in natural blue sapphire

The differences described for synthetic sapphires apply equally to the star varieties. In the synthetic version the colour is usually much brighter and the star more sharply defined than in the natural stone.

Alexandrite

Synthetic alexandrite is a true copy of the rare chrysoberyl variety, and unlike the corundum and spinel simulants, exhibits the exact colour change of natural alexandrite (i.e. pale green in daylight to a brownish-red in incandescent light). It is made by both Czochralski and flux melt processes, and although it has all the physical characteristics of fine Siberian alexandrite, the RI is reported to be 0.02 lower than that of the natural variety. Under the microscope, the synthetic appears to be characterised by swarms of tiny inclusions (apparently parallel to the seed face), similar to those found in synthetic emeralds and flux-grown rubies; banding or growth lines can also be seen.

Opal

The 'Gilson' synthetic opals are produced as both white and black stones. Of these, the white opal is the most convincing. The black version, however, should cause no identification problem to anyone familiar with the natural product. Under a high-magnification (60×) microscope, the structure lines within the yellow colour segments of the older type white Gilson opal resemble a series of closely spaced gullies reaching down from each side of a central spine. The structure within an orange segment of the newer white Gilson opal, however, has a crazy-paving appearance.

Gilson opals are made from sodium silicate or a silicon ester which is then slowly dehydrated. The tiny particles produced are similar to the cristobalite spheres in natural opal, and as they are extremely small (0.0002 mm diameter), they are only visible with the aid of a high-power instrument such as an electron microscope. In both synthetic and natural stones these spheres are arranged in regular rows of similar size and produce the opal's play of colour by means of diffraction and interference of the reflected light (see *Figure 2.6* in Chapter 2).

Features distinctive of the Gilson opals which can be seen with the aid of a microscope have been summarised by Messrs E. A. Jobbins, P. M. Statham and K. Scarratt as follows:

(1)   The stones show a mosaic comprising equidimensional or 'blocky' structures viewed from above or below.

(2)   Many white synthetics show a pronounced columnar structure when viewed from the side.

(3)   Some white synthetics show a distinctive dendritic structure at higher magnifications in transmitted light.

(4)   Under transmitted light the grains often have finely crenulated edges giving them a 'dried leaves' effect.

(5)   In later black and white opals the grains have a 'lizard skin' appearance seen under magnification by both transmitted and reflected light.

(6)   Many Gilson opals have high porosity, and tend to stick to the tongue. This effect is not so marked in many natural stones.

It is also possible on occasions to use opal's luminescent properties to separate natural opals from Gilson synthetics. As all samples of Gilson synthetic opals fluoresce a 'dusty' green colour (similar to that shown by paste imitations) under SW UV, and a few fluoresce under LW UV, any opals which show *no* signs of fluorescence under LW or SW UV are natural opals.

When a natural opal *does* fluoresce under UV (usually with a white or cream shade) it also phosphoresces. This phosphorescence, as viewed under dark conditions, continues for a period of approximately twelve seconds. Signs of phosphorescence are virtually non-existent in darker Gilson specimens.

It has also been noted that in the columnar structure of synthetic opals, the colour in each column is the same in any direction. In the rare natural specimens which show a columnar structure, the colour varies from point to point.

Spinel

Like synthetic corundum, synthetic spinel is produced mainly by the Verneuil 'flame fusion' process. As the colours in which synthetic spinels are produced are intended to simulate those of the more expensive gemstones, they are generally quite different from those found in natural spinels. Fortunately, because of the large amount of alumina used in the growth of the synthetic spinel boule, its physical properties are markedly different from those of natural spinel:

Natural spinel	*Synthetic spinel*
RI = 1.717	RI = 1.727
SG = 3.6	SG = 3.64

A refractive index test therefore forms a positive means of identifying a suspect stone. In addition, because of the method of manufacture, synthetic spinels often contain internal stresses which are revealed as an anomalous birefringence under a polariscope. This is a patchy cross-hatched variation in light transmission which occurs when rotating the stone between crossed polars, and has been aptly named 'tabby extinction' by B. W. Anderson.

Although spinels of a wide variety of colours have been made by the Verneuil method, red ones are rare as they tend to fracture at the boule stage.

Spinels have also been grown by the flux melt process, and these include red spinels which, unlike their natural counterparts, do not show the typical fluorescent 'organpipe' spectral lines.

Diagnostic inclusions in natural spinels are tiny spinel octahedron crystals (in Burma reds), which form a ghost-like feather, and spinel crystals arranged in lines (in stones from Sri Lanka — *Figure 11.5(f)*). Spherical gas bubbles may occasionally be seen in synthetic spinel.

Turquoise

Gilson synthetic turquoise under 50× magnification is seen to be composed of small dark blue angular particles in a white background 'matrix', a structure quite unlike that seen in natural turquoise.

The specific gravity of one sample Gilson turquoise was found to be in the region of 2.635 (compared with 2.8 for natural) and its RI was 1.592 (compared with 1.62). Other samples have averaged 2.74 and 1.60 respectively. Unfortunately, both of these constants are characteristic of natural turquoise from America, and it would seem that the best test that can be made is a visual examination (at about 50×) for the characteristic dark blue particles in a whitish groundmass exhibited in Gilson synthetic turquoise.

Lapis lazuli

Gilson synthetic lapis lazuli has as its chief ingredient the mineral lazurite (which is also one of the constituents of the natural rock). In a destructive test, the crushing of Gilson lapis produces a strong sulphurous smell, unlike its natural counterpart; in addition, the synthetic version reacts far more strongly to a spot of hydrochloric acid than does the natural lapis, and its SG is much lower.

A series of tests made on both synthetic and natural lapis lazuli has shown that the synthetic version has a relatively high porosity (natural lapis has none), is less dense than natural (SG is approximately 2.36 compared with 2.8) and that it reacts more rapidly to sulphuric, nitric and hydrochloric acids. Because of its relatively high porosity, it has been more accurately described in some literature as a lapis substitute.

Mr H. Andersen has given the following hints for recognising the Gilson synthetic lapis lazuli:

(1)   A very good violet-blue colour, comparable with the finest lapis lazuli.

(2)   A better lustre than the natural lapis (more like sodalite).
(3)   The pyritic inclusions can be scratched with a needle.
(4)   The white inclusions are like longish clouds, not comparable to the natural inclusions.
(5)   The 'streak' (made by rubbing a fragment against a piece of white unglazed porcelain, called a *streak plate*) is dark blue instead of light blue.
(6)   X-rays show it as an amorphous (X-ray transparent) substance.

Quartz

Synthetic quartz is grown hydrothermally, and has been produced for many years for the optical and electronic industries. More recently, both the Americans and the Russians have manufactured quantities of gem quality quartz in gem colours. As the cost of the synthetic quartz is close to that of the natural variety, there is less concern in the identification of a synthetic quartz gem, except perhaps for the amethyst variety. This is fortunate, as their physical properties are, as might be expected, identical (natural amethyst has a 'tiger-stripe' inclusion).

The colourless seed plate is usually visible in uncut synthetic quartz material, and this is accompanied by strong colour banding parallel to the plate. Breadcrumb-like inclusions may also be visible (*Figure 11.5(e)*).

12 Gemstone Simulants

In contrast to synthetic gemstones, which have the same chemical composition, crystal system and physical constants as their natural counterparts, a simulant need only have a superficial resemblance to the gemstone it imitates. Materials used to simulate the more costly gem minerals range from natural gemstones (sometimes dyed) to various man-made products. Their detection and identification is usually straightforward, as their physical constants are hardly ever the same as those of the gemstone they imitate. Mounted diamond simulants are probably the most troublesome, as their refractive indices are usually above the range of the standard refractometer. For this reason, they have been dealt with in some depth in the following notes, which also indicate the characteristics to look for in simulants of the more valuable coloured gemstones.

Alexandrite simulants

Both synthetic corundums and synthetic spinels have been produced which imitate the characteristic colour change seen in the alexandrite variety of chrysoberyl. However, where alexandrite changes from a pale greenish colour in daylight to a brownish-red in incandescent light, most synthetic corundums (doped with vanadium and chromic oxides) change from a washed-out greyish-blue in daylight to an amethyst-purple in tungsten light. The synthetic spinel version is less common, and although it matches the alexandrite colour change more closely, spinel is singly-refracting and therefore has no pleochroism. The strong pleochroism in alexandrite (red, orange, green in

194

tungsten light) also distinguishes it from that of the corundum simulant (brownish-yellow, purple in tungsten light).

The specific gravity of alexandrite (3.72) is higher than that of spinel (3.64) and lower than that of corundum (4.0). Although alexandrite and corundum have similar RIs (1.746 to 1.755 and 1.760 to 1.768 respectively), spinel (1.727) can easily be identified on the standard refractometer.

Aquamarine simulants

Apart from paste simulants and composite stones (which are described under separate headings), the most commonly used aquamarine simulant is synthetic blue spinel. A simple test on a polariscope (taking care not to be misled by the strain patterns often seen in spinel) will separate the doubly-refracting aquamarine from the singly-refracting spinel. A more positive identification can be made on the refractometer (RI for aquamarine = 1.570 to 1.575; RI for synthetic spinel = 1.727).

With an unmounted stone, aquamarine will float in bromoform, while spinel will sink. Because synthetic blue spinel is coloured by cobalt it will appear red through a Chelsea colour filter (see under 'Emerald simulants'), while aquamarine will appear green. Aquamarine also shows green as well as blue through the dichroscope, but spinel being singly-refracting has no pleochroism.

Diamond simulants

Because of its beauty and value, diamond is probably the most imitated of all the gemstones. Unlike emerald and ruby, whose values sometimes exceed even that of diamond, there are as yet no commercially available synthetic gem quality diamonds, although both the Americans and the Russians have produced laboratory-grown one carat crystals.

Natural simulants of diamond include the colourless varieties of quartz, topaz, corundum and zircon, all of which can be distinguished from diamond by virtue of their double refraction.

With the exception of zircon, it is possible to identify all of these stones by means of a simple refractometer reading. This test can also be used to distinguish diamonds from colourless synthetic spinels and corundums, and from paste. Other even simpler optical tests are described at the end of this section.

The beauty of a polished diamond depends on its dispersion (0.044) and its lustre. It also depends on the optical design of the brilliant-cut stone, which ensures that as much light as possible entering the stone is reflected back through the crown facets. The high adamantine lustre of a polished diamond is, in turn, dependent upon the stone's hardness (10.0 in the Mohs scale) and its high refractive index (2.42).

The design of the brilliant-cut diamond has evolved over many years, and has resulted in a set of ideal proportions and angles (see *Figure 7.11*). These have been selected, mainly by trial and error, to exploit diamond's high refractive index and dispersion, and form the basis of the 'light-spill' and 'light-transmission' tests used to distinguish diamond from its simulants.

To match diamond's fire and brilliance, a simulant must therefore have a reasonably high dispersion and a high refractive index. It should also be as hard as possible and singly-refracting (like diamond) if it is to have a reasonable chance of escaping detection.

Flint glass was probably the first man-made diamond simulant, although its use in antique jewellery was possibly due to its pleasing degree of 'fire' (dispersion = 0.04) rather than its superficial resemblance to diamond. With the exception of synthetic colourless corundums and spinels, which were introduced as simulants almost fifty years ago, the majority of man-made simulants are spin-offs from specialised crystals developed for the electronics and laser industries. The most important of these will now be described.

Synthetic rutile ('rainbow gem', 'titania' – TiO_2)

Synthetic rutile has a noticeable yellow tinge, which, coupled with its excessive 'fire' (dispersion = 0.28) makes it a relatively poor diamond simulant. Its large double refraction (0.287) also makes it easily distinguishable by eye or on a polariscope.

YAG ('diamonaire', 'diamonique' – $Y_3Al_5O_{12}$)

This is an yttrium aluminium garnet, which has no counterpart in nature. Its low refractive index (1.83) and dispersion (0.028) combine to give it a 'lifeless' appearance. Its best features are its hardness (8.5) and its singly-refracting cubic crystal structure.

Strontium titanate ('diagem', 'fabulite' – $SrTiO_3$)

This is another man-made material with no counterpart in nature. It has almost the same refractive index as diamond (2.41), and because of this cannot be detected by the 'light-spill' and 'light-transmission' tests. However, as its dispersion (0.190) is over four times that of diamond, it is easily identified by its excessive 'fire'. Another identifying feature is its hardness (5.5), which is low enough for it to be scratched by a steel needle (although a hardness test of this nature cannot be recommended). However, the relative softness of strontium titanate can still provide useful diagnostic information, as described in the 'facet condition' test at the end of this section.

Lithium niobate ('linobate' – $LiNbO_3$)

Lithium niobate has almost three times the dispersion of diamond. It has a high refractive index (2.25), but a large double refraction (0.09). These factors, coupled with its low hardness value (5.5), combine to make it a poor simulant.

GGG ($Gd_3Ga_5O_{12}$)

Another man-made simulant which does not appear in nature, gadolinium gallium garnet has a high refractive index (1.97) and a dispersion close to that of diamond (0.045). Its only weak feature is its relatively low hardness value (6.0).

Cubic zirconium oxide ('diamonesque', 'djevalite', 'phianite', 'zirconia' – ZrO$_2$)

At the time of writing, this is the most convincing diamond imitation to have appeared. With a refractive index of 2.16, a dispersion of 0.065 and a hardness of 8.5, cubic zirconium oxide has a better combination of physical constants than any other commercial simulant (see *Table 12.1* for comparative list of constants). In its unmounted state it can easily be identified, as its specific gravity is 5.7 compared with diamond's 3.52. With a brilliant-cut stone, this can be done by comparing the weight of the stone with its girdle diameter (see *Table 12.2*).

Table 12.1

Gemstone	RI	DR	Dispersion	SG	Hardness
diamond	2.42	–	0.044	3.52	10.0
paste (flint glass)	1.6–1.7	–	0.04	3.0–4.0	5.0
synthetic spinel	1.727	–	0.02	3.64	8.0
synthetic corundum	1.76–1.768	0.008	0.018	4.0	9.0
synthetic rutile	2.61–2.897	0.287	0.28	4.2	6.5
YAG	1.83	–	0.028	4.58	8.5
strontium titanate	2.41	–	0.19	5.13	5.5
lithium niobate	2.21–2.30	0.09	0.120	4.64	5.5
GGG	2.02	–	0.038	7.05	6.0
cubic zirconium oxide	2.16	–	0.06	5.7	8.5

Table 12.2

Girdle diameter (mm)	Cubic zirconium oxide (carat)	Diamond (carat)
3.0	0.22	0.12
6.5	1.75	1.0
9.0	4.6	2.5

Despite its high refractive index it can usually be distinguished from diamond by the 'light-spill' and 'light-transmission' tests. Under SW UV, it fluoresces either a greenish-yellow or a distinct yellow, while diamonds are generally inert.

Tests to distinguish diamond from its simulants

(1) 'Light spill' test   If a brilliant-cut stone (mounted or unmounted) is viewed against a dark background, with the table facet at right-angles to the line of vision, the stone will appear uniformly bright because its pavilion facets will act as reflecting mirrors.

If the stone is a diamond, it will be possible to tilt it (so that the eye begins to look into the table facet at increasingly shallow angles) without losing the uniformly bright appearance of the pavilion facets, even when this angle becomes very small ($5°$ to $10°$). If the stone is a simulant, and has a lower refractive index than diamond, the pavilion facets furthest from the eye will begin to look black as the stone is tilted below $60°$ (i.e. light will 'spill' out of these facets instead of being reflected back). The lower the refractive index of the stone, the more marked will be the effect.

(2) 'Light-transmission' test   If the stone is an unmounted one, and is placed table facet downwards on a coloured surface, the colour will not show through the back of the pavilion facets if the stone is a diamond or a strontium titanate.

(*Note*: Tests 1 and 2 are effective only for modern round brilliants, and rely on the fact that nearly all simulants are cut to the same ideal proportions as diamond. If a round brilliant-cut stone passes these tests, but has a very deep pavilion, it should be suspect. Older diamonds may have the small table facet and deep pavilion of the 'Old English' cut, and will not pass these two tests).

(3) The 'facet condition' test   Diamond is the hardest of natural substances, and this makes it possible to achieve a very

high degree of polish on its facets. Because of its hardness, it is also possible to polish the facets so that they are perfectly flat and meet each other at sharply defined edges. Softer stones will not have the same high degree of polish and their facet edges will be more rounded. If the stone has been worn for several years, it may also be possible to detect signs of damage or wear at the facet edges.

(4) 'Refractive index/reflectivity' tests   The refractive indices of some simulants (synthetic spinel and synthetic corundum) are low enough to be measured on a standard refractometer. For simulants whose refractive indices are above the range of the refractometer, it is generally possible to make an identification by measuring their lustre on an electronic reflectivity meter (see Chapter 7).

Emerald simulants

When emerald simulants first began to appear in quantity, a simple test instrument called the *Chelsea colour filter* (*Figure 12.1*) was developed jointly by the Gem Testing Laboratory of

Fig. 12.1. The Chelsea colour filter combines a red and a yellow filter to match the spectral characteristic of emerald (Gemmological Instruments Ltd.)

the London Chamber of Commerce and the Chelsea College of Science and Technology to provide a means of separating the natural stone from its simulants. The filter consists of a combination of two gelatine filters designed to transmit only deep red and yellow-green light. This combination was chosen to match the unusual spectral characteristic of emerald, which transmits light in the deep red, but absorbs it in the yellow-green.

When a collection of green stones is strongly illuminated and viewed through the filter, the genuine emeralds (including synthetic emeralds) will appear distinctly red or pinkish in colour (depending on the depth of colour of the emerald), while faceted green glass (i.e. paste), doublets and *soudé* emeralds will appear green (see under 'Composite stones').

Unfortunately the filter is not foolproof. There are a few emeralds, in particular those from South Africa, which may not appear red or pink through the filter. As already indicated, synthetic emeralds react in the same way as natural ones, although their colour appears more brilliant. Demantoid garnet and green zircon also appear pinkish through the Chelsea filter, but both of these produce 'negative' readings on the refractometer (i.e. they are above its range), and unlike emeralds will sink when immersed in bromoform.

Green tourmaline, especially when heat treated, may occasionally be used as an emerald simulant. Although some green tourmalines contain chromium, and, like emerald, appear pink through the Chelsea filter, they can be easily identified by taking a refractometer reading (RI for tourmaline = 1.62 to 1.64; RI for emerald = 1.579 to 1.585). Emerald will float in bromoform, while tourmaline will sink.

Jade simulants

There are many simulants of the true jade minerals jadeite and nephrite. Among these are hydrogrossular garnet (known as 'Transvaal jade'), bowenite, amazonite and the chrome—mica impregnated clay, verdite. Apart from the differences between the constants of these simulants and jadeite/nephrite (see *Table 12.3*), Jadeite can sometimes be identified under the spectroscope by means of an intense absorption band visible in the violet at 437 nm. Jadeite also has a characteristic dimpled or 'orange peel' surface when polished. As with other cryptocrystalline substances, jadeite is capable of being dyed, and

Table 12.3

Gemstone	RI	SG	Hardness
jadeite	1.65−1.67	3.3	7.0
nephrite	1.61	3.0	6.0
hydrogrossular	1.73	3.48	6.5
bowenite	1.56	2.58	4.0
amazonite	1.53−1.54	2.56	6.0
verdite	1.58	2.9	3.0

poorly coloured specimens may often be dyed green. Dyed jadeite tends to appear pinkish when viewed through the Chelsea filter, unlike natural green jadeite. When examined under the spectroscope the dye produces an indistinct absorption band in the red, and the jadeite band at 437 nm is missing.

Lapis lazuli simulants

'Swiss lapis', a fairly common simulant of lapis lazuli, is made by colouring jasper with 'Prussian blue' pigment. It can be identified by its lack of pyrite inclusions and its slightly higher refractive index (1.54 compared with 1.5 for genuine lapis). Another simulant is sodalite, which is a constituent of lapis. This can be distinguished by its specific gravity (lapis = 2.8; sodalite = 2.28).

A more expensive lapis lazuli simulant was made by the German Degussa company in 1954. This was a sintered form of synthetic spinel, made by heating a mixture of alumina, magnesia and cobalt to a temperature just below the melting point of spinel. The result is a coarse-textured material closely resembling lapis lazuli in colour. Gold flakes are said to have been included in the mix to imitate the pyrite inclusions in the natural rock. This may have been because the process was not compatible with the introduction of pyrite flakes (as used in Gilson synthetic lapis).

Ruby simulants

Natural stones which may be used to imitate ruby include garnets (pyrope and almandine), spinel, tourmaline, zircon and possibly pink topaz. *Table 12.4* lists the constants of these

Table 12.4

Gemstone	RI	DR	SG	Hardness
ruby	1.76–1.77	0.008	4.0	9.0
pyrope	1.75–1.77	–	3.7–3.8	7.5
almandine	1.77–1.81	–	3.8–4.2	7.5
spinel	1.717	–	3.6	8.0
tourmaline	1.62–1.64	0.018	3.01–3.11	7.0
topaz	1.63–1.64	0.008	3.53	8.0
zircon	1.93–1.99	0.058	4.68	7.25

simulants together with those of ruby. From this it is possible to deduce the most reliable tests to use for identification purposes (see also under 'Paste simulants' and 'Composite stones').

Pyrope garnet is the one stone which may prove difficult by eye to distinguish from ruby. However, pyrope's complete lack of dichroism, together with the difference in the absorption spectra of the two stones (see *Figure 8.4*) and their dissimilar responses under the polariscope will serve to identify and separate them.

In general, ruby can be identified by its bright red appearance under the Chelsea filter, and by its intense red fluorescence under LW and SW UV light. The garnets (containing iron) and red tourmaline (coloured by manganese) do not fluoresce at all under UV, nor do they appear red through the filter. Red spinel, like ruby, is coloured by chromium, and cannot be separated by these two tests. However, its absorption spectra, lack of dichroism, refractive index reading and single refraction response on the polariscope should enable it to be easily distinguished from ruby.

Sapphire simulants

While sapphire is imitated by both paste and composite stones, the most convincing simulants are blue synthetic spinel and a few of the natural blue gemstones. Among the latter is the blue variety of zoisite. In its mined state, this gemstone has very strong pleochroism, which gives it distinctive purple tints. To make blue zoisite imitate sapphire more closely, it is heat treated. This reduces its pleochroism and lightens the stone's colour. Despite its deceptive appearance, zoisite can easily be distinguished from sapphire by its refractive index, which is 1.69 to 1.70 (compared with sapphire's 1.76 to 1.77).

Another natural simulant, iolite (sometimes called dichroite or cordierite), is easily identified by its very strong dichroism (hence its alternative name 'dichroite'), and its low refractive index (1.54 to 1.55). Blue tourmaline can also be identified by means of its refractive index (1.62 to 1.64) and by its relatively large double refraction (0.018).

Synthetic blue spinel makes a convincing sapphire simulant, but it is easily identified by means of its refractive index (1.727), its strong cobalt absorption spectra (see *Figure 8.4*) and its response on the polariscope (allowing for the possibility of anomalous birefringence caused by internal stresses). The cobalt content of synthetic blue spinel causes it to appear pink or red under the Chelsea filter, and this test acts as a positive indication of a fake stone, as there are no naturally-occurring transparent blue gemstones which show this colour.

Turquoise simulants

As this gem material is a semi-translucent crypto-crystalline substance, it can sometimes be difficult to separate it positively from its simulants, which include paste, coloured plaster of Paris, odontolite, stained porcelain, stained bone, chalcedony and howlite.

The two main ways of distinguishing genuine turquoise from its simulants are to inspect the surface of the suspect gem under the microscope, and to check its absorption spectrum with a spectroscope. The surface of turquoise shows small irregular particles of white material in a pale homogeneous blue matrix, and is significantly different from the appearance of all its simulants. It is often lined or banded with black or brown traces of limonite matrix. The lustre of paste, porcelain and chalcedony is vitreous compared with the more waxy appearance of turquoise. Bubbles may also be present in paste and porcelain. Bone simulants have a greasy lustre, and the internal bone channels show at any break in the surface. Other distinguishing features are shown in *Table 12.5*.

Table 12.5

Gemstone	RI	SG	Hardness
turquoise	1.61–1.65	2.6–2.8	6.0
chalcedony	1.53–1.54	2.58–2.64	6.5
howlite	–	2.53–2.59	3.5
odontolite	–	3.0–3.5	5.0

The absorption spectrum of turquoise contains a strong narrow band in the violet at 432 nm, and a broader less distinct band at 460 nm, neither of which can be seen in any of the turquoise simulants. As these bands are in the violet/blue end of the spectrum where the eye is less sensitive, it helps if the specimen is illuminated with blue-filtered incident light.

Paste simulants

Apart from its use as a diamond simulant, glass can be coloured to match most of the more common gemstones. Sapphire blue pastes are usually coloured with cobalt, and show red when viewed through the Chelsea colour filter. One tell-tale check for glass is to look for signs of bubble inclusions, or colour swirls, with the aid of a microscope. As glass is rather brittle, and relatively soft, there will also tend to be damage, perhaps in the form of characteristic conchoidal fractures, to the facet edges.

Glass is amorphous, and a paste simulant will therefore be singly-refracting, and will never show dichroism, which will serve to distinguish it from some of the stones it simulates. As there is no singly-refracting natural gemstone which falls within the range of RIs covered by pastes (1.50 to 1.70), an RI test can also be confirmatory (see also note on p. 100).

Composite stones

Except for the rare case where a composite stone is formed by two sections (crown and pavilion) of the same mineral (which are cemented together to form a larger whole), and opal doublets and triplets, these stones are usually fabricated with the intent to deceive.

Composite stones can consist of doublets, whose crown can be of the mineral being faked, and whose pavilion can be of a cheaper mineral, such as quartz, or even a synthetic (i.e. a diamond crown and a YAG or synthetic white sapphire pavillion – see *Figure 12.2*).

Opal doublets are formed from a thin top layer of precious opal backed with common or potch opal, the latter being hidden by the mount. Opal triplets are formed by cementing a dome of clear quartz to the thin top layer of a opal doublet. In this case, the top of the composite stone shows no sign of irridescence, and a 'distant vision' RI reading for quartz can be obtained from this face.

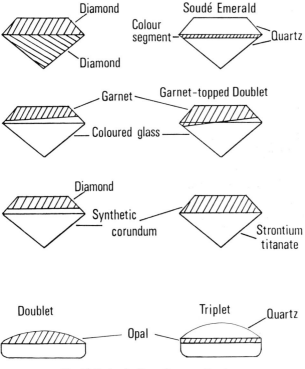

Fig. 12.2. A selection of composite stones

A range of doublets has been produced using a coloured glass pavilion to which is fused a thin crown section of garnet. These are described as garnet-topped doublets. The high garnet lustre of the table enables them to simulate ruby, blue sapphire, emerald, peridot, citrine and topaz, with the appropriately coloured glass pavilion. They are easily identified by the high RI reading of the table facet, by the presence of bubbles and colour swirls in the glass pavilion, and by other typical composite-stone characteristics (referred to in the next paragraphs).

Triplets, such as the soudé emerald, consist of a quartz, a synthetic white spinel, or a colourless beryl top, with a quartz base. The colouring element completing the triplet consists of a thin layer of gelatine or sintered glass cemented or fused between the crown and pavilion sections. When immersed in water and inspected in line with the girdle, both crown and pavilion sections can be seen to be colourless.

Although it is convenient to form a doublet or triplet with the join around the girdle (which can be more easily hidden by the mounting) it is possible to find the join higher up the crown. RI readings of the crown will usually reveal the fraud (except in those cases where the crown is of the simulated gem material), Careful examination of the stone immersed in

Fig. 12.3. Immersing a garnet-topped doublet in monobromonaphthalene (or water) makes the two separate components clearly visible

monobromonaphthalene (or water) will usually show any differences in body colour between the two halves (*Figure 12.3*). Because of the porosity of opal, this test should not be used with opal doublets or triplets, neither should a liquid other than water be used with any composite stone which has been cemented rather than fused.

Fig. 12.4. Careful orientation of both the stone and the light source is necessary to reveal the join between the crown and pavilion sections of a doublet

Further examination of the stone with a hand loupe, or under a microscope, will reveal the junction (*Figure 12.4*). This may also be indicated by a plane of bubbles where the two halves have been fused or cemented together.

Perhaps the most important composite stone these days is the diamond doublet. This is made from a thin crown of diamond cemented to a pavilion which can be a variety of materials from quartz to one of the man-made simulants of diamond (such as synthetic corundum, YAG, GGG, or zirconia).

Occasionally one sees a synthetic doublet in which a crown of YAG or synthetic corundum has been cemented to a pavilion of strontium titanate in order to 'quench' the excess 'fire' of the latter, and provide a harder wearing top surface. The result is more like a diamond than a stone made completely from either material, but with the availability of cubic zirconium oxide as a convincing diamond simulant such a substitute is probably no longer an economic proposition.

Appendix A

Gemstone profiles. Inclusions in natural and man-made gems

(See Appendix B for constants and crystal systems, and Chapter 7 for pleochroism. For **Amber, Coral, Ivory, Jet, Mother-of-pearl, Odontolite, Pearl, Tortoiseshell**—*see Chapter 10).*

Principal gem minerals

Beryl — $Be_3Al_2(SiO_3)_6$. Vitreous. *Varieties,* goshenite (colourless), emerald (green), aquamarine (pale blue or sea green), heliodor (yellow), morganite (pink). *Cleavage,* imperfect parallel to basal pinacoid. *Occurrence,* emerald in metamorphic rocks (limestone and marble); other beryls in pegmatites. Goshenite from USA; emeralds from Brazil, Columbia, India, Pakistan, Russia, Rhodesia, South Africa; aquamarines from Brazil, Russia and the Malagasy Republic. Heliodor from Brazil, the Malagasy Republic and Namibia. Morganite from Brazil, the Malagasy Republic, Rhodesia and Namibia.

Chalcedony — SiO_2 (crypto-crystalline quartz). Vitreous. *Varieties,* chalcedony (unbanded greys and blues), agate (all colours with curved concentric bands), onyx (black and white, straight banding), cornelian (red or brown), chrysoprase (apple green), bloodstone or heliotrope (dark green with spots of red jasper). *Occurrence,* in cavities in volcanic rocks, or as nodules in sedimentary rocks. Deposits are world-wide.

Chrysoberyl — $BeAl_2O_4$. Vitreous. *Varieties*, alexandrite (green in daylight, red in incandescent light), cymophane (yellowish cat's eye), chrysoberyl (green, yellow, brown). *Cleavage*, imperfect. *Occurrence*, as alluvial pebbles. Alexandrite historically from Russia, main sources now are Sri Lanka and Rhodesia; other varities from Brazil, Burma and Sri Lanka.

Corundum – Al_2O_3. Vitreous. *Varieties*, ruby (red), sapphire (colourless, blue, green, yellow, pink, purple and orange). *Cleavage*, none, but parting parallel to basal pinacoid. *Occurrence*, in crystalline limestone or as alluvial pebbles. Sapphire from Burma, Thailand, Cambodia, Sri Lanka, Kashmir, Australia, USA (Montana); ruby from Burma, Thailand, Sri Lanka, Tanzania.

Diamond – Carbon. Adamantine. *Varieties*, colourless and shades of yellow (Cape series), brown and green (also 'fancy' shades of pink, orange, yellow, brown, blue, green); industrial diamonds of poor colour and quality, including boart, carbonado and frasmasite. *Cleavage*, easy, parallel to octahedral faces. *Occurrence*, in volcanic pipes and as secondary alluvial deposits. Found first in India and then in Brazil. Main sources now Southern Africa, Russia, and China.

Feldspar group – *Species*, orthoclase and microcline, $KAlSi_3O_8$; plagioclase, $(Ca,Na)Al_2Si_2O_8$. Vitreous to pearly (moonstone). *Varieties*, orthoclase (moonstone, translucent with adularescence; orthoclase, pale yellow), microcline (amazonite, opaque green/blue-green), plagioclase (oligoclase, yellow; labradorite, multi-coloured iridescence; sunstone, gold-spangled; adventurine feldspar, green with spangles; albite moonstone, yellowish translucent with chatoyance or asterism). *Cleavage*, easy to perfect. *Occurrence*, in intrusive igneous rocks. Orthoclase from Burma and the Malagasy Republic; moonstone from Sri Lanka, Burma, Brazil, India, Tanzania, USA; amazonite from USA, Namibia, Russia; oligoclase, sunstone and aventurine feldspar from USA, Canada, India, Russia; labradorite from Canada. Australia, Russia, Finland ('spectrolite').

Garnet group – *Species*, pyrope (blood red) $Mg_3Al_2(SiO_4)_3$, vitreous; almandine (purplish-red) $Fe_3Al_2(SiO_4)_3$, vitreous; grossular (see varieties) $Ca_3Al_2(SiO_4)_3$, greasy; andradite (see varieties) $Ca_3Fe_2(SiO_4)_3$, adamantine; spessarite (orange, yellow, flame red) $Mn_3Al_2(SiO_4)_3$, vitreous; uvarovite (emerald green) $Ca_3Cr_2(SiO_4)_3$, vitreous. *Varieties,* grossular (hessonite, orange-brown, green, pink; massive grossular and hydrogrossular, jade green), andradite (demantoid, green; topazolite, yellow). *Cleavage,* none. *Occurrence,* mainly as dodecahedron crystals in matrix. Pyrope from Czechoslovakia, USA, South Africa; almandine from Czechoslovakia, Sri Lanka, the Malagasy Republic, Brazil and Australia; grossular from Canada, USSR, Sri Lanka (hessonite), South Africa (hydrogrossular), USA (hessonite) and Pakistan; andradite from Russia (demantoid), Switzerland (topazolite), Italy (topazolite); spessartite from Sri Lanka, USA, Brazil, the Malagasy Republic; uvarovite from Russia, Finland, Poland, USA, Canada.

Jadeite — $NaAlSi_2O_6$. Waxy. *Varieties,* white, yellow, brown, green, mauve, black. (As translucent green 'Imperial Jade' it is more valuable than the other jade mineral, nephrite). *Cleavage,* none. *Occurrence,* in boulders or conglomerates, usually interlayered with serpentine. Also in alluvial gravels. Burma.

Lapis lazuli — Opaque rock composed of sodalite, lazurite, calcite, haüynite, with spangles of pyrite. Vitreous to greasy. *Varieties,* blue, colour evenly distributed in best quality; often interspersed with veins of white calcite. *Cleavage,* none. *Occurrence,* in white dolomitic marble. Afghanistan, Russia, Chile.

Nephrite — Complex silicate of iron, magnesium and calcium. Greasy. *Varieties,* white, yellow, but mainly a dark green. *Cleavage,* none. *Occurrence,* in boulders and conglomerates, often interlayered with serpentine. Also as alluvial pebbles. China, New Zealand.

Opal — $SiO_2.nH_2O$. Waxy. *Varieties,* common or 'potch' opal (opaque without iridescence), white opal (white background with iridescence), black opal (dark background with iridescence), fire opal (translucent to transparent orange, rarely iridescence), water opal (translucent to transparent, colourless or brownish-yellow with adularescence). *Cleavage,* none. *Occurrence,* as solidified veins of silica gel in sandstone or clay matrix (precious opal), or in limonite matrix (common opal). Australia, Mexico (fire opal).

Peridot – $(Mg,Fe)_2 SiO_4$. Vitreous. *Varieties*, bright apple-green, olive green, brownish(rare). *Cleavage*, imperfect. *Occurrence*, in cavities in peridotite rock, or gravels derived from them. Also in serpentine deposits. Isle of St John in the Red Sea. Burma.

Quartz – SiO_2. Vitreous. *Varieties,* rock crystal (colourless), amethyst (purple), citrine (yellow), rose quartz (semi-translucent pink), jasper (opaque, red/brown), aventurine quartz (opaque green or golden-brown with spangles of mica), quartz cat's eye (colourless, yellow-brown or green with chatoyance), tiger's eye (golden yellow or brown with chatoyance), hawk's eye (blue variety of tiger's eye). *Cleavage*, none. *Occurrence*, in igneous rocks and cavities and in alluvial geodes. Deposits are world-wide, except for tiger's eye and hawk's eye which come principally from South Africa.

Spinel – $MgAl_2 O_4$. Vitreous. *Varieties*, all colours including yellow (colourless spinels are rare). *Cleavage*, imperfect. *Occurrence*, in metamorphic rocks and gravels. Burma, Sri Lanka, Thailand.

Topaz – $Al_2(F,OH)_2 SiO_4$. Vitreous. *Varieties,* colourless and yellow to sherry-brown; blue and blue-green (natural pink stones are rare, but can be produced by heat treatment of yellow or brown stones). *Cleavage*, perfect, parallel to basal pinacoid. *Occurrence*, in granite rocks, in pegmatites and as alluvial pebbles. Brazil, Sri Lanka, Russia, Burma.

Tourmaline – Complex boro-silicate of aluminium and other metals, Vitreous. *Varieties*, achroite (colourless), indicolite (blue), schorl (black), dravite (brown), verdelite (green). Also yellow, pink and multi-/parti-coloured. *Cleavage,* none. *Occurrence*, in pegmatites, granite rocks and alluvial deposits. Sri Lanka, the Malagasy Republic, Brazil, USA, and Namibia.

Turquoise – Complex hydrated phosphate of copper and aluminium. Waxy. *Varieties*, blue, blue-green and green. Often patterned with traces of brown or black matrix. *Cleavage*, none. *Occurrence*, as veins or nodules in limonite or sandstone matrix. Iran, Tanzania, USA, Australia, China.

Zircon — $ZrSiO_4$. Adamantine ('normal'), vitreous ('low'). *Varieties*, colourless, yellow, brown, orange, red, blue, green. (Brown stones heat treated in absence of oxygen to produce blue zircon, or in air to produce colourless, orange or golden-brown stones.) *Cleavage,* imperfect. *Occurrence*, as alluvial pebbles and as crystals in igneous rocks. Sri Lanka, Cambodia, Burma, Thailand, Australia.

Secondary Gem Minerals (chemical composition and colour — see Appendix B for constants and crystal systems, and Chapter 7 for pleochroism)

Andalusite — Al_2SiO_5. Green (chiastolite variety is opaque yellowish-white with back cross). **Apatite** — Calcium phosphate with fluorine or chlorine. Blue, yellow (rare earth spectrum due to didymium), pink, violet, green. **Benitoite** – $BaTi(SiO_3)_3$. Light and dark blue. **Bowenite** — Hydrated magnesium silicate. Opaque green. **Danburite** — $CaB_2(SiO_4)_2$. Colourless, golden, pink. **Diopside** — $CaMg(SiO_3)_2$. Green. **Enstatite** – $MgO.SiO_2$. Green, brownish-green (transparent to opaque). (Perfect cleavage). **Fluorspar** – CaF_2. Colourless, blue, violet, green, yellow, orange, red. (Perfect cleavage; fluorescence strong in most varieties — none in 'Blue John'). **Haematite** – Fe_2O_3. Opaque black, blackish-grey, brown-red. **Idocrase** — Complex calcium aluminium silicate. Olive-green, yellowish-brown. **Iolite** — Complex silicate of magnesium and aluminium. Shades of blue. **Kornerupine** — $MgAl_2SiO_6$ (Al may be replaced by Fe or B). Greyish-green, green-brown, bright green. **Malachite** — Cu_2 $(OH_2)CO_3$. Opaque banded light and dark green. (Perfect cleavage). **Moldavite** — $SiO_2 + Al_2O_3$. Bottle green, brown-green. (Natural glass in tektite group). **Obsidian** — mainly silica. Black, brown, dark green. (Volcanic glass). **Phenakite** — Be_2SiO_4. Colourless, yellowish, pink. **Pyrite** — FeS_2. Brass yellow, grey-yellow. **Rhodochrosite** — $MnCO_3$. Opaque to transparent red with white banding. (Perfect cleavage). **Rhodonite** — $MnSiO_3$. Opaque to transparent red with black banding. (Perfect cleavage). **Scapolite** – Aluminium silicate with

Na and Ca. Blue, pink, yellow. (Perfect cleavage). **Scheelite** — $CaWO_4$. Yellow, brown, colourless. Transparent to translucent. **Sinhalite** — $Mg(Al,Fe) BO_4$. Greenish-brown, golden brown. (Distinguished from peridot by extra absorption band at 463 nm, and a negative instead of positive optic sign). **Smithsonite** — $ZnCO_3$. Translucent pink, light green or blue. (Perfect cleavage). **Sodalite** — Chloric sodium aluminium silicate. Opaque to translucent blue with white patches or veins. (perfect cleavage). **Spodumene** — $LiAl(SiO_3)_2$. Pale green, yellow, pink/purple (kunzite variety), yellow-green to chrome-green (hiddenite variety). (Perfect cleavage). **Steatite** (soapstone) — Acid meta-silicate of magnesium. Opaque yellow, brown, reddish. **Titanite** (sphene) — $CaTiSiO_5$. Yellow, golden-brown, emerald green. (Perfect cleavage). **Zoisite** — Silicate of calcium and aluminium. Opaque green, transparent blue (tanzanite), opaque red (thulite).

Inclusions in natural gemstones
(See also Chapter 11 and *Figures 11.5* and *11.7*)

Garnet	*Pyrope* — Zircon crystals with 'haloes'.
	Almandine — Crossed needles of hornblende. Apatite. Rutile (giving star effect). Zircon crystals with 'haloes'.
	Hessonite — Profuse diopside crystals of good shape. 'Treacle'.
	Demantoid — Asbestos fibres forming 'horse-tails'.
	Spessartite — Liquid shreds.
Aquamarine	Negative crystals (liquid filled voids). Flags (liquid patches), more often seen in green beryl. 'Rain'. Two-phase inclusions.
Amethyst	'Tiger stripe' inclusions and colour zoning.

Iolite	Red haematite platelets ('bloodshot' iolite).
Moonstone	Stress cracks looking like centipedes.

Peridot
- *Hawaiian* — Liquid discs looking like water lilies.
- *Arizonan* — Long liquid bubbles.
- *Isle of St John* — Magnetite octahedra.

Quartz	Rutile needles, and tourmaline prisms.
Spinel	Spinel octahedra in Burma reds (forming ghost-like feather).
	Spinel crystals in Sri Lanka stones (in chains).
Topaz	Liquid-filled cavities, containing immiscible liquids. Interference colours generated by internal cleavages. Two-phase and three-phase inclusions.
Tourmaline	Tourmaline crystals. Liquid-filled cavities. Profuse 'negative' crystals (voids). Actinolite crystals.
Zircon	Zircon inclusions (low green zircons have colour zones or paralleled fine lines).

Inclusions in man-made gemstones
(See also Chapter 11 and *Figures 11.5* and *11.6*)

Quartz (hydrothermal process)
> Blue, green and yellow quartz grown from a seed crystal may show the colourless seed inside. Strong colour banding.

Lechleitner emerald (hydrothermal coating of a faceted piece of poor colour beryl)
> Discontinuity of inclusions between overgrowth and base material. Network of surface cracks.

Vanadium beryl (hydrothermal process)
> Colour banding (no chromium lines, absorption band in orange).

Chatham, Gilson and Zerfass emeralds (flux melt process)
> Veil-like feathers.

Appendix B

GEMSTONE CONSTANTS
(In alphabetical order of gemstone)

Gemstone	Crystal system	Approx. RI	DR	Dispersion	SG	H
alexandrite – see chrysoberyl						
almandine (garnet)	cubic	1.77–1.81	–	0.027	3.8–4.2	7.5
amber	amorphous	1.54	–	–	1.05–1.10	2.5
amazonite (feldspar)	triclinic	1.53–1.54	0.008	0.012	2.56	6.0
andalusite	orthorhombic	1.63–1.64	0.01	0.016	3.18	7.5
andradite (demantoid, melanite topazolite-garnet)	cubic	1.89	–	0.057	3.85	6.5
apatite	hexagonal	1.63–1.64	0.003	0.013	3.18–3.22	5.0
aquamarine – see beryl						
benitoite	trigonal	1.76–1.80	0.047	0.04	3.65–3.68	6.5
beryl (aquamarine, emerald, goshenite, heliodor)	hexagonal	1.57–1.58	0.006	0.014	2.71	7.5–8.0
bowenite	monoclinic	1.56	*	–	2.58	4.0
chalcedony	trigonal	1.53–1.54	*	–	2.58–2.64	6.5
chrysoberyl (alexandrite, cymophane)	orthorhombic	1.74–1.75	0.009	0.014	3.72	8.5
coral	trigonal	–	*	–	2.6–2.7	3.5
cordierite – see iolite						
corundum (ruby, sapphire)	trigonal	1.76–1.77	0.008	0.018	4.0	9.0
cubic zirconium oxide	cubic	2.18	–	0.065	5.7	8.5
cymophane – see chrysoberyl						

Gemstone	Crystal system	Approx. RI	DR	Dispersion	SG	H
danburite	orthorhombic	1.63–1.64	0.006	0.016	3.0	7.0
demantoid – see andradite						
diamond	cubic	2.42	–	0.044	3.52	10.0
dichroite – see iolite						
diopside	monoclinic	1.67–1.70	0.03	–	3.3	5.0
emerald – see beryl						
enstatite	orthorhombic	1.66–1.67	0.01	–	3.25–3.30	5.5
feldspar – see amazonite, moonstone, oligoclase, orthoclase, sunstone						
fluorspar	cubic	1.43	–	0.007	3.18	4.0
garnet – see almandine, andradite, grossular, pyrope, spessartite, uvarovite						
GGG	cubic	1.97	–	0.045	7.05	6.0
goshenite – see beryl						
grossular (hessonite-garnet)	cubic	1.74	–	0.027	3.65	6.5
haematite	trigonal	2.94–3.22	0.28	–	4.9–5.3	5.5–6.5
heliodor – see beryl						
hessonite – see grossular						
hiddenite – see spodumene						
idocrase	tetragonal	1.70–1.72	0.005	0.019	3.32–3.42	6.5
iolite (cordierite, dichroite)	orthorhombic	1.54–1.55	0.008	0.017	2.57–2.61	7.5
ivory (dentine)	amorphous	1.54	–	–	1.70–2.00	2.0–3.0
ivory (vegetable)	amorphous	1.54	*	–	1.38–1.54	2.5
jadeite	monoclinic	1.65–1.67	–	–	3.33	7.0
jet	amorphous	1.66	–	–	1.3	3.5

kornerupine	orthorhombic	1.67–1.68	0.013	0.018	3.28–3.35	6.5
kunzite — see spodumene						
lapis lazuli	—	1.50	—	—	2.8	5.5
lithium niobate	trigonal	2.21–2.30	0.09	0.120	4.64	5.5
malachite	monoclinic	1.66–1.91	0.25	—	3.8	4.0
melanite — see andradite						
moldavite	amorphous	1.50	—	—	2.53	5.5
moonstone and orthoclase (feldspar)	monoclinic	1.52–1.53	0.006	—	2.57	6.0
morganite	hexagonal	1.58–1.59	0.008	0.014	2.85	7.5–8.0
nephrite	monoclinic	1.61	*	—	2.97	6.0
obsidian	amorphous	1.50	—	0.01	2.4	5.0
odontolite	amorphous	—	—	—	3.0–3.25	5.0
oligoclase (feldspar)	triclinic	1.53–1.54	0.007	—	2.64	6.0
opal	amorphous	1.45	—	—	2.1	6.0
orthoclase — see moonstone						
pearl	orthorhombic	1.52–1.66	—	—	2.71–2.74	3.5–4.0
peridot	orthorhombic	1.65–1.69	0.038	0.02	3.34	6.5
phenakite	trigonal	1.65–1.67	0.016	0.015	2.95–2.97	7.5
pyrite	cubic	—	—	—	4.84–5.10	6.5
pyrope (garnet)	cubic	1.75–1.77	—	0.022	3.7–3.8	7.5
quartz	trigonal	1.54–1.55	0.009	0.013	2.65	7.0
rhodonite	triclinic	1.73–1.74	0.012	—	3.6–3.7	6.0
rhodochrosite	trigonal	1.60–1.82	0.22	—	3.5–3.6	4.0
ruby — see corundum						
rutile	tetragonal	2.61–2.90	0.287	0.28	4.2–4.3	6.5
sapphire — see corundum						
scapolite (blue)	tetragonal	1.54–1.56	0.016	0.017	2.60–2.71	6.0
scapolite (pink, yellow)	tetragonal	1.56–1.58	0.02	0.017	2.60–2.71	6.0

Gemstone	Crystal system	Approx. RI	DR	Dispersion	SG	H
scheelite	tetragonal	1.92–1.93	0.016	0.026	5.9–6.1	4.5
sinhalite	orthorhombic	1.67–1.71	0.038	0.018	3.48	6.5
soapstone – see steatite						
sodalite	cubic	1.48	–	–	2.28	5.5–6.0
smithsonite	trigonal	1.62–1.85	0.23	–	4.30	5.0
spessartite (garnet)	cubic	1.80	–	0.027	4.16	7.0
spinel (natural)	cubic	1.717	–	0.020	3.60	8.0
spinel (synthetic)	cubic	1.727	–	0.020	3.64	8.0
sphene – see titanite						
spodumene (hiddenite, kunzite)	monoclinic	1.66–1.68	0.015	0.017	3.18	7.0
steatite (soapstone)	monoclinic	1.54–1.59	0.05	–	2.5–2.8	1.0+
strontium titanate	cubic	2.41	–	0.19	5.13	5.5
sunstone (feldspar)	triclinic	1.53–1.54	0.009	–	2.64	6.0
tanzanite – see zoisite						
titanite (sphene)	monoclinic	1.89–2.02	0.13	0.051	3.53	5.5
topaz (white/blue)	orthorhombic	1.61–1.62	0.01	0.014	3.56	8.0
topaz (brown/yellow)	orthorhombic	1.63–1.64	0.008	0.014	3.53	8.0
topazolite – see andradite						
tourmaline	trigonal	1.62–1.64	0.018	0.017	3.01–3.11	7.0
turquoise	triclinic	1.61–1.65	*	–	2.6–2.8	6.0
uvarovite (garnet)	cubic	1.87	–	–	3.77	7.5
YAG	cubic	1.83	–	0.028	4.58	8.5
zircon (normal)	tetragonal	1.93–1.99	0.058	0.039	4.68	7.25
zircon (low-green)	amorphous	1.78–1.84	–	–	3.9–4.1	6.0
zirconia – see cubic zirconium oxide						
zoisite (tanzanite – blue zoisite)	orthorhombic	1.69–1.70	0.009	0.03	3.35	6.5

*

GEMSTONE CONSTANTS
(In order of refractive indices)

Approx. RI	DR	Gemstone	Crystal system	Dispersion	SG	H
1.43	—	fluorspar	cubic	0.007	3.18	4.0
1.45	—	opal	amorphous	—	2.1	6.0
1.48	—	sodalite	cubic	—	2.28	5.5–6.0
1.50	—	lapis lazuli	—	—	2.8	5.5
1.50	—	obsidian	amorphous	0.01	2.4	5.0
1.50	—	moldavite	amorphous	—	2.53	5.5
1.52–1.53	0.006	moonstone and orthoclase (feldspar)	monoclinic	—	2.57	6.0
1.52–1.66	—	pearl	orthorhombic	—	2.71–2.74	3.5–4.0
1.53–1.54	0.008	amazonite (feldspar)	triclinic	—	2.56	6.0
1.53–1.54	*	chalcedony	trigonal	—	2.58–2.64	6.5
1.53–1.54	0.007	oligoclase (feldspar)	triclinic	—	2.64	6.0
1.53–1.54	0.009	sunstone (feldspar)	triclinic	—	2.64	6.0
1.54	—	amber	amorphous	—	1.05–1.10	2.5
1.54	—	ivory (dentine)	amorphous	—	1.70–2.00	2.0–3.0
1.54	—	ivory (vegetable)	amorphous	—	1.38–1.42	2.5
1.54–1.55	0.009	iolite (cordierite, dichroite)	orthorhombic	0.017	2.57–2.61	7.5
1.54–1.55	0.009	quartz	trigonal	0.013	2.65	7.0
1.54–1.56	0.016	scapolite (blue)	tetragonal	0.017	2.60–2.71	6.0
1.54–1.59	0.05	steatite (soapstone)	monoclinic	—	2.5–2.8	1.0+
1.56	*	bowenite	monoclinic	—	2.58	4.0
1.56–1.58	0.02	scapolite (pink/yellow)	tetragonal	0.017	2.60–2.71	6.0
1.76–1.80	0.047	benitoite	trigonal	0.04	3.65–3.68	6.5
1.57–1.58	0.006	beryl (aquamarine, emerald, goshenite, heliodor, morganite)	hexagonal	0.014	2.71	7.5–8.0

Approx. RI	DR	Gemstone	Crystal system	Dispersion	SG	H
1.60–1.82	0.22	rhodochrosite	trigonal	–	3.5–3.6	4.0
1.61	*	nephrite	monoclinic	–	2.97	6.0
1.61–1.62	0.01	topaz (white/blue)	orthorhombic	0.014	3.56	8.0
1.61–1.65	*	turquoise	triclinic	–	2.6–2.8	6.0
1.62–1.64	0.018	tourmaline	trigonal	0.017	3.01–3.11	7.0
1.62–1.85	0.23	smithsonite	trigonal	–	4.3	5.0
1.63–1.64	0.01	andalusite	orthorhombic	0.016	3.18	7.5
1.63–1.64	0.003	apatite	hexagonal	0.013	3.18–3.22	5.0
1.63–1.64	0.006	danburite	orthorhombic	0.016	3.0	7.0
1.63–1.64	0.008	topaz (brown/yellow)	orthorhombic	0,014	3.53	8.0
1.65–1.67	*	jadeite	monoclinic	–	3.33	7.0
1.65–1.67	0.016	phenakite	trigonal	0.015	2.95–2.97	7.5
1.65–1.69	0.038	peridot	orthorhombic	0.02	3.34	6.5
1.66	–	jet	amorphous	–	1.34	3.5
1.66–1.67	0.01	enstatite	orthorhombic	–	3.25–3.30	5.5
1.66–1.68	0.015	spodumene (kunzite, hiddenite)	monoclinic	0.017	3.18	7.0
1.66–1.91	0.25	malachite	monoclinic	–	3.8	4.0
1.67–1.68	0.013	kornerupine	orthorhombic	0.018	3.28–3.35	6.5
1.67–1.70	0.03	diopside	monoclinic	–	3.3	5.0
1.67–1.71	0.038	sinhalite	orthorhombic	0.018	3.48	6.5
1.69–1.70	0.009	zoisite	orthorhombic	0.003	3.35	6.5
1.70–1.72	0.005	idocrase	tetragonal	0.019	3.32–3.42	6.5
1.717	–	spinel (natural)	cubic	0.020	3.6	8.0
1.727	–	spinel (synthetic)	cubic	0.020	3.64	8.0
1.73–1.74	0.014	rhodonite	triclinic	–	3.6–3.7	6.0
1.74	–	grossular (hessonite-garnet)	cubic	0.027	3.65	6.5
1.74–1.75	0.009	chrysoberyl (alexandrite, cymophane)	orthorhombic	0.014	3.72	8.5

RI	Birefringence	Name	Crystal system	Dispersion	SG	Hardness
1.75–1.77	—	pyrope (garnet)	cubic	0.022	3.7–3.8	7.5
1.76–1.77	0.008	corundum (ruby, sapphire)	trigonal	0.018	4.0	9.0
1.77–1.81	—	almandine (garnet)	cubic	0.027	3.8–4.2	7.5
1.78–1.84	—	zircon (low-green)	amorphous	—	3.9–4.1	6.0
1.80	—	spessartite (garnet)	cubic	0.027	4.16	7.0
1.83	—	YAG	cubic	0.028	4.58	8.5
1.87	—	uvarovite	cubic	—	3.77	7.5
1.89	—	andradite (demantoid, topazolite-garnet)	cubic	0.057	3.85	6.5
1.89–2.02	0.13	titanite (sphene)	monoclinic	0.051	3.53	5.5
1.92–1.93	0.016	scheelite	tetragonal	0.026	5.9–6.1	4.5
1.93–1.99	0.058	zircon (normal)	tetragonal	0.039	4.68	7.25
1.97	—	GGG	cubic	0.045	7.05	6.0
2.18	—	cubic zirconium oxide	cubic	0.065	5.7	8.5
2.21–2.30	0.09	lithium niobate	trigonal	0.120	4.64	5.5
2.41	—	strontium titanate	cubic	0.19	5.13	5.5
2.42	—	diamond	cubic	0.044	3.52	10.0
2.61–2.90	0.287	rutile	tetragonal	0.28	4.2–4.3	6.5
2.94–3.22	0.28	haematite	trigonal	—	4.9–5.3	5.5–6.5

* crypto-crystalline

Units of measurement

Weight   The standard international (SI) unit of weight is the kilogram (kg). The most frequently used subdivisions are the gram and the milligram.

> 1 kilogram = 1000 grams
> 1 gram   = 1000 milligram

= 0.03527 ounce Avoir (1 ounce Avoir = 28.349 gram)
= 0.03215 ounce Troy (1 ounce Troy = 31.103 gram)

For gemstone weighing, the standard unit is the metric carat.

1 carat
 = 0.2 gram (1 gram = 5 carats)
 = 0.007055 ounce Avoir (1 ounce Avoir = 141.747 carats)
 = 0.006430 ounce Troy (1 ounce Troy = 155.517 carats)

For pearl weighing, the standard unit is the grain or the carat.

1 grain = 0.25 carats (1 carat = 4 grains)

Note: The weight of small rough diamonds is sometimes expressed in grains (e.g. a 1.0 carat stone may be called a 'four grainer').

Polished diamonds under 1.0 carat in weight are measured in points.

1 point = 0.01 carat (1 carat = 100 points)

Length   The standard international (SI) unit for the measurement of length is the metre (m). The most frequently used subdivisions are the centimetre (cm), millimetre (mm), micrometre (μm, previously called 'micron') and nanometre (nm).

$$1m = 100 \text{ cm}$$
$$1cm = 10 \text{ mm} = 10^{-2} \text{ m}$$
$$1mm = 1000 \,\mu\text{m} = 10^{-3} \text{ m}$$
$$1 \,\mu\text{m} = 1000 \text{ nm} = 10^{-6} \text{ m}$$
$$1 \text{ nm} = 10^{-9} \text{ m}$$

Wavelength   The standard international (SI) unit for the measurement of light wavelengths is the nanometre (nm).

$1 \text{ nm} = 10^{-9} \text{ m}$ (one thousand-millionth of a metre)
$1 \text{ nm} = 10 \text{ Å}$ (ångström units)

Light wavelengths are also sometimes given in microns or micrometres (μm)

$$1 \,\mu\text{m} = 1000 \text{ nm} = 10\,000 \text{ Å}$$

Temperature   The standard international (SI) unit for temperature is the Kelvin (K), and the degree Celsius (°C), both of which span equal temperature intervals. The Kelvin is used mainly for thermodynamic work, and represents an *absolute* temperature.

$$0\,^{\circ}\text{C} = 273.16\text{K}$$
$$0 \text{ K} = - 273.16\,^{\circ}\text{C}$$

(At zero degrees Kelvin no more internal energy can be extracted from an object, and the volume of a gas is theoretically zero.)

Miller indices

Crystallographic indices provide a means of identifying the position and orientation of a crystal face in terms of the axes cut by the face, and the distances from these intercepts to the origin. These distances do not have to be quantified, but can be taken as ratios one to another.

Crystal faces are often parallel to one or more axes, and therefore only meet them theoretically at infinity. The indices of the most commonly used system (devised by W. H. Miller) are based on the reciprocal of these ratios (the reciprocal of infinity being, conveniently, zero).

In a cubic crystal, the six crystal faces are cut by the axes x, y, z (*Figure B.1(a)*). The crystal face shown in *Figure B.1(b)* is given the Miller index (001) because it is parallel to the x axis (intercept ratio = infinity, reciprocal = 0), and to the y axis (= 0), but is intersected by the z axis (= 1). The same face on the opposite side of the crystal (*Figure B.1(c)*) is identified as (00$\bar{1}$), as with the Miller system an intercept on an axis pointing away from the observer is given a negative index ($\bar{1}$). The two faces intercepted by the y, $-y$ axis are coded (010) and (0$\bar{1}$0). The remaining two faces, intercepted by the x, $-x$ axis, are identified as (100) and ($\bar{1}$00).

Four of the eight faces of an octahedron are similarly identified in *Figure B.1(f)*, and *Figure B.1(g)* shows the Miller indices for cubic and rhombic dodecahedron *planes* in the same crystal.

When an index is enclosed by brackets, this indicates a crystal face, as in (100). If the index is enclosed in *braces*, this indicates a form comprising all the faces generated by that index. For example, $\{100\}$ denotes a cube, and $\{111\}$ denotes an octahedron. Used without brackets or braces, an index indicates a plane within the crystal (as illustrated by 001 and 110 in *Figure B.1(g)*.).

The index of the crystal face also indicates its angle relative to the z axis. For example, the faces of a cube-derived octahedron are identified by (111), and intercept the z axis at 45° (i.e. all the intercepts are equidistant from the origin). If, however, the faces met the z axis at a distance $z/2$ from the origin, the inverse ratios would produce an index of (112) for these faces.

The Miller index system was subsequently adapted by A. Bravais to suit the four-axis hexagonal/trigonal system. With crystals in this system, faces are generally identified by means of Miller–Bravais indices. The sequence of the four axes in

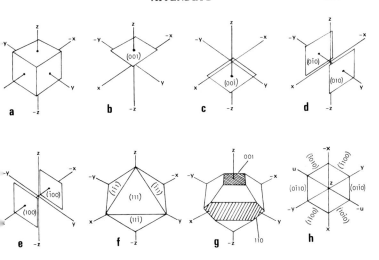

Fig. B.1. Examples of the coding of crystal faces and planes by Miller indices

this case is x, y, u, z, and their polarities are arranged as indicated in *Figure B.1(h)*. Each prism face in the first order hexagonal prism (shown in plan view in *Figure B.1(h)*) is intercepted by two of the three lateral axes x, y, u, and the prism faces are each identified by a *four figure* index, $(1\bar{1}00)$, $(10\bar{1}0)$, $(01\bar{1}0)$, $(\bar{1}100)$, $(\bar{1}010)$ and $(0\bar{1}10)$. The indices for the two faces of the terminating basal pinacoid are (0001) and $(000\bar{1})$.

For the sake of simplicity, *Figure B.1(h)* only shows the prism face indices for a first order prism. In a *second order* hexagonal prism, the prism faces are each 'bisected' at their centres by one of the lateral axes x, y, u. The extended plane of each prism face is also intercepted by the remaining two lateral axes at a distance from the origin which is exactly *twice* the length of the single bisecting axis. The reciprocals of the ratios for these indices are therefore in the form $(2\bar{1}\bar{1}0)$, $(11\bar{2}0)$, $(\bar{1}2\bar{1}0)$, etc., starting with the face bisected by the x axis.

Appendix C
Bibliography

Diamonds, by E. Bruton, NAG Press
Elements of Mineralogy, by F. Rutley, Thomas Murby and Co.
From the World of Gemstones, by H. Bank, Pinguin-Verlag (Argus Books Ltd)
Gemmological Instruments, by P. G. Read, Newnes-Butterworths
Gemmologists Compendium, By R. Webster, NAG Press
Gems, by R. Webster, Newnes-Butterworths
Gems in Jewellery, by R. Webster, NAG Press
Gemstones, by G. F. Herbert Smith, Chapman & Hall
Gemstones for Everyman, by B. W. Anderson, Faber
Gemstones of the World, by W. Schumann, NAG Press
Gem Testing, by B. W. Anderson, Newnes-Butterworths
Handbook of Gem Identification, by R. T. Liddicoat, GIA
Internal World of Gemstones, by E. Gübelin, Newnes-Butterworths
Minerals, Rocks and Precious Stones, by J. Bauer, Octopus Books
Practical Gemmology, by R. Webster, NAG Press
Textbook of Mineralogy, Dana, John Wiley & Sons (Chapman & Hall)
The History and Use of Diamond, by S. Tolansky, Methuen
The Magic of Amber, by R. Hunger, NAG Press
The Encyclopedia of Minerals and Gemstones, by M. O'Donoghue, Orbis Publishing Ltd

Gemmological, mineral and gemstone books are available from:

The Gemmological Association of Great Britain, St. Dunstan's House, Carey Lane, London EC2V 8AB

Mineral Associates, 8 Clarence Place, Clapton Square, London E5

Appendix D
Examination Notes

These notes have been compiled specifically to help students who are preparing for the Preliminary or Diploma examinations of the Gemmological Association of Great Britain.

Theory papers

Both first and second year examinations have two theory papers, each containing five questions. Unlike some other professional examinations, there is no choice of questions, and to achieve high marks (or a comfortable pass) it is necessary to be familiar with the complete syllabus. Two and a half hours are allocated for answering each paper.

Despite the inevitable feeling that it is impossible to do justice to all five questions in the time, students are strongly advised to spend the first five minutes in reading through the question paper carefully, and making sure exactly what is being asked of them in each question. Among the subjects covered by the questions there will be those which the student is more confident at answering, and those which may cause problems. Psychologically, it is a good plan to answer the 'easiest' questions first in order to gain confidence, and to leave the more difficult ones to the last. If this plan is followed, a reasonably strict timetable should be adopted, allocating twenty-five minutes for answering each question. If five minutes are used to read and understand the questions at the start of the examination, this will leave twenty minutes at the end for checking over the answers, and making sure that they are complete.

One of the pitfalls in all examinations is the possibility of misunderstanding the questions, and although these are carefully written using the least ambiguous phrasing, it is still advisable to prepare for the event by becoming familiar with the contents and style of papers set in previous years. Copies of earlier papers can be obtained from the offices of the Gemmological Association (see page 228 for address). Despite the shortage of time, some effort should be made to write legibly. Examiners are human, and the readability of the answer paper should not be allowed to fall to the point where communication between the candidate and the examiner is in danger of breaking down!

Practical paper

For many students, particularly those taking the correspondence course, the practical examination can be more difficult than the theory papers. The examination lasts three and a half hours, and falls into four parts, which include the identification of five crystal specimens by visual inspection alone, the precise measurement of the refractive index and double refraction of five polished specimens, the identification of ten polished gemstones using the equipment provided, and the identification of a further five specimens mainly by the use of the spectroscope. As with the theory paper, time is the enemy, and a maximum of seven to eight minutes should be allowed for each determination. The remaining time at the end of the exam can then be spent in checking over answers and in re-testing any doubtful specimens.

As the efficient functioning of the eyes is most important when examining specimens (both with the hand lens and with the optical instruments) it is advisable to keep out of bright sunlight just before taking the exam, and to allow the eyes to become semi-dark adapted. A card containing a printed list of gemstone constants is provided for each candidate at the practical exam, but as it is necessary to know these facts for the theory papers, it is probably more time conserving to use this list only for 'back-up' information.

Even with the best organised practical examination, it is possible for 'bottlenecks' to occur with the use of instruments, and the candidate must be prepared to use his time to best advantage by making tests out of sequence if necessary.

Index